Clinical Hypnosis

A guide for practical intervention

Ursula James
Honorary Lecturer
St George's Medical School, London
and
Visiting Teaching Fellow
Oxford University Medical School

Foreword by

Mark Feldman

Radcliffe Publishing
Oxford • Seattle

Radcliffe Publishing Ltd
18 Marcham Road
Abingdon
Oxon OX14 1AA
United Kingdom

www.radcliffe-oxford.com
Electronic catalogue and worldwide online ordering facility.

British Library Cataloguing in Publication Data

A catalogue record for this book is available from the British Library.

ISBN   1 85775 725 4

Typeset by Wordspace, Lewes, East Sussex
Printed and bound by T J International, Padstow, Cornwall

Contents

Foreword

It only happens rarely, perhaps three or four times in a lifetime of attending lectures – the hairs stand up on the back of the neck, you experience a sense of wonder and a sudden need to discover more about the subject that is almost a physical craving.

This is what I felt when I first heard Ursula James lecture on the introductory course for clinical hypnosis.

Ursula is a natural teacher and has distilled the essence of clinical hypnosis into this new text. Theory, however, is all very well but it carries little weight if practical skills are lacking. It is in this aspect of the work that she excels. When discussing a hypnotherapeutic puzzle with her there is a sense that, instead of merely looking at the patient and finding an option for treatment, she walks around the problem viewing it from all angles to arrive almost magically at the best solution.

I remember vividly one case that I referred to her, of a young woman at a business meeting far from home who had awoken to find a stranger in her hotel bedroom. She talked to him for six hours before he finally left her. During this time she was in constant fear of physical attack.

I first saw her three weeks later when she was still unable to talk without crying and could barely leave home. I referred her to Ursula and after one session she was back at work – the trauma behind her. She had no further problems. I am convinced that conventional counselling or medication could not have accomplished this almost miraculous transformation.

Of course it was not a miracle – but the application of hypnotherapeutic techniques by a master practitioner, Ursula James.

This wide-ranging primer covers the theory, practice and history of the subject, as well as including very useful links to further information.

This fascinating subject is made accessible by her clearly structured approach and everyone who reads it, from novices to experienced hypnotherapists, is sure to gain new insights from the book.

Mark Feldman
President
British Association of Medical Hypnosis
March 2005

Introduction

Clinical hypnosis is a useful personal tool for stress management, goal setting and relaxation. It can also be an excellent addition to the range of professional techniques for anyone working within the caring professions. Hypnosis creates a relaxation state, the therapeutic component allows the patient to access positive states, and it can also be used as a stress reduction mechanism, as well as enhancing the patient's responsiveness to change. These are some of the benefits over and above its use within a formal protocol. One area often overlooked and is elemental in clinical hypnosis – the use of stylised language techniques. These can be utilised in patient evaluation, to enhance diagnostic skills, and also to improve general communication.

This book gives an overview of the subject of clinical hypnosis and sets out to introduce the reader to the potential for its application within the medical setting. In addition, it teaches individuals how to experience self-hypnosis and induce it to others. It further explores the framework of a session, and breaks down the individual components and how they are constructed to create a unique therapeutic protocol using specific language patterns. Lastly, this volume gives an overview of the historical context of clinical hypnosis and the current variations and schools of thought on its application, alongside a glossary of terms and list of useful contacts and websites.

It can be used as an introduction to the subject, or for the experienced practitioner to gain a wider understanding of the ways in which sessions are constructed. The use of specific language in patient communication and therapeutic evaluation is discussed at some length, and this can be used outside the framework of a formal clinical hypnosis session whenever patient evaluation skills are required. Specific techniques for the more common conditions where clinical hypnosis can be effective are also covered in some detail at the end of the volume.

Acknowledgements

Dr Lyn Williamson, for giving me the opportunity to design and present the first clinical hypnosis course at Oxford University Medical School.

Thomas Connelly, Secretary of the British Society of Clinical Hypnosis, for creating the glossary of terms and list of useful website addresses, and allowing it to be replicated for this volume.

Dedication

My family – for always believing in me.

Michael Joseph – for his extraordinary teaching.

Phil Benjamin – for changing my mind.

Dr Mark Feldman – for his boundless enthusiasm.

Chapter 1

What is hypnosis?

The term 'hypnosis' derived originally from the Greek god of sleep, Hypnos, who was the father of Morpheus, god of dreams. In the 1800s, James Braid coined the term 'neurypnosis', which he believed to be a form of paralysis of the central nervous system that occurred during a sleep-like state. The term was subsequently shortened to 'hypnosis'. There have been many changes in the definitions of hypnosis since then, from theories that suggest it is a form of mind control, or a symptom of hysteria, through to the current, more practical definition which identifies it as a structured therapeutic tool. The subject of clinical hypnosis, although it has been around for many years on the periphery of medical application is in a renaissance thanks to advances in MRI and CAT scanning. Hypnosis is now being systematically researched as a viable medical intervention – free from any known side-effects, cost-effective and time-efficient.

The first thing to be aware of is that a hypnotic experience is a conscious experience. The individual is aware and in control throughout. It is a usually a pleasant experience, often involving relaxation, and there will be times during the process when the individual feels less aware of surroundings and more aware of internal events. After the experience, the individual will often notice time distortion – with a feeling that the perceived time was much shorter than clock time. Rather than being unfamiliar, hypnosis can be defined as an extension, or amplification, of normal states of awareness.

The experience each person has will be unique, and will depend on a number of factors: previous experience, expectations and motivation, to name a few. Hypnosis can be difficult to define even when you have experienced it. This is for two reasons: first, because it takes place in the internal environment and we therefore do not have the language to communicate it fully. It is the same when you try to describe your dreams to another person; the telling is a pale reflection of what happened to you. Second, it is hard to describe because each patient's encounter with hypnosis is different, depending on that person. It is not, however, sleep.

Hypnosis is often defined by what it is *not*. It is not sleep, it is not like a general anaesthetic and it is not unlike some other familiar states of awareness. One of the first things that occurs during a clinical hypnosis session is that the practitioner will ask the patient what they know about hypnosis. Once the practitioner has a clear picture of the patient's current understanding of hypnosis, the practitioner will then select a model to describe the experience to the patient in a way which will best help them to experience it. Models are frequently used in clinical hypnosis sessions as ways of providing a framework for patients to feel comfortable, or become more receptive to suggestions. Models will take what patients previously understood about the process and re-interpret it in a way that will allow them to obtain the maximum benefit from the event.

Hypnosis has often been defined, even by the medical community, by one of the misconceptions most commonly held, that it is not a 'real' event, only a perceptual change. In this volume we will discuss the physiological phenomena of the hypnotic state. In addition, the influence of suggestions given in this state and how it creates changes in both psychological and organic-based conditions will also be described and explained.

The *Encarta Dictionary* defines 'hypnosis' as follows.

hyp•no•sis [hip nŏssiss] (plural hyp•no•ses [hip nŏ seèz])

noun
1.   sleep-like condition: a sleep-like condition that can be artificially induced in people, in which they can respond to questions and are very susceptible to suggestions from the hypnotist
2.   putting people in sleep-like condition: the technique or practice of inducing a state of hypnosis in people. Also called <u>hypnotism</u>

The term 'hypnotherapy' is defined as follows.

hyp•no•ther•a•py [hŸpnō thérrapee]

noun
treating illness with hypnosis: the use of hypnosis in treating illness, for example, in dealing with physical pain or psychological problems

The term 'clinical hypnosis' is now more commonly used to denote a specific treatment protocol. It is the use of hypnosis or the hypnotic state, in a medical framework, for the alleviation of physical, psychological or behavioural problems. Clinical hypnosis employs a protocol whereby the technique selected correlates directly to information collected from the case history. This lends itself more readily to research and, in theory, is replicable regardless of practitioner.

- 'Hypnosis' is a physical and mental state of highly focused concentration.
- 'Hypnotherapy' is the process of inducing hypnosis and making suggestions to a patient for a therapeutic purpose.
- 'Clinical hypnosis' incorporates a range of defined and replicable methodologies within the hypnotic state, including physical relaxation and a state of mental focus and receptiveness to assist the patient to take control of their condition and effect a change.

This volume will refer to the term 'hypnosis' when referring to the state, the term 'hypnotherapy' when referring to the process and the term 'clinical hypnosis' when referring to therapeutic application or the use of a specific protocol.

A natural phenomenon

The state of hypnosis can be simply explained as a naturally occurring phenomenon during which the body remains relaxed while the mind goes into a highly focused state. In the course of an ordinary day we may enter hypnotic-like states many times, and for varying reasons. When bored or not fully engaged with our current surroundings our system has a way of distracting ourselves by daydreaming about things that we would like to do in our future, or going into a state of reverie to re-experience pleasant events from our past. If we are in physical pain, or traumatised by an event we can also shift our awareness. This ability to dissociate is a protective mechanism, and, as with daydreams and reverie, is a completely natural process. Whichever way, we become disconnected from our immediate surroundings and can shift our current mood, or ability to interact with our surroundings. The protocols of clinical hypnosis engage and enhance individuals' ability to relax and alter their current state. Clinical hypnosis takes processes and events which are already part of the individual's experience of the world, and utilises them to create positive change. In hypnosis the individual becomes focused and receptive to positive suggestions. Generally, the attention is directed towards pre-experiencing or re-experiencing positive states and outcomes. As a result individuals begin to feel more optimistic, and start to direct their attention on to potential change. There are some therapeutic protocols which actively promote the re- or pre-experiencing of unpleasant or anxiety-inducing states. Even with these protocols, the therapeutic emphasis remains on the individual's capacity to experience something different from this, that is, more positive and beneficial.

In addition to the passive states of daydream and reverie, there are learnt activities, such as driving a car, which become automatic. Driving on 'auto-pilot' is sometimes known as 'highway hypnosis', and occurs usually when a route is so familiar that we do not need to 'think' about where we are going. On occasion it appears as if our body is carrying out the behaviour while our mind is elsewhere. It is the body (or, some would term, the unconscious mind's) ability to carry out functions without conscious processing of information, and is a very useful capacity. The individual's ability to store and retrieve information when required is very useful with regard to habits and learnt behaviours. It does, however, make it more difficult if the individual wishes to change that unconscious pattern.

This capacity for automatic activity (that is, without conscious or deliberate thought) occurs most commonly when we are in familiar surroundings or easily recognised moods. This explains the higher incidence of accidents closer to, or even in, the home. As individuals feel comfortable and do not need to 'think' about their surroundings, they are not on alert when a change occurs – hence the increased response time, and higher rate of accidents. When individuals are hypnotised they are encouraged to focus on the familiar events of the hypnotic state so they will recognise and feel comfortable, therefore activating the state of low conscious activity, or automatic processing. Patients will often state on awakening that they 'did not feel as if they were hypnotised' precisely because the state is already a familiar one and they often expect something very different. In clinical hypnosis, this capacity to be relaxed in familiar surroundings is used to encourage patients to access their unconscious capabilities.

The third component of clinical hypnosis, which again is a naturally occurring event, is the capacity of hypnosis to enhance the mind's ability to access emotional variations by use of memory or prediction. This natural capacity to add emotion to events can have a positive or negative effect. Mark Twain once remarked, 'I have known many troubles in my life, and most of them never happened.' This highlights the way in which individuals have a tendency to predict, and often with a negative outcome if they are feeling lacking in confidence. Once emotion has been added to a memory that memory becomes much stronger and more intense. If the emotion associated with a memory subsides, the capacity to recall that memory will be reduced.

In summary, the hypnotic state helps the patient to access the following:

- the passive events of daydreaming and reverie
- an increased focus attention on unconscious activity
- influence future by accessing positive memory associations.

In turn, the occurrence of these three natural events is enhanced by hypnotic suggestion. This, in turn, increases patients' capacity to:

- pre-experience or re-experience an event
- utilise their unconscious functionality to stay calm and relaxed
- produce a positive emotion or response.

> Clinical hypnosis uses naturally occurring states and behaviours and amplifies them.

Hypnotic suggestions

The first element to understand about hypnotic suggestions is that these are suggestions based only on the discussion between the patient and practitioner before formal induction of hypnosis takes place. Suggestions are refined, clarified and agreed by the patient. If a practitioner decided to add suggestions that were not previously agreed with the patient, they would automatically pull themselves out of the hypnoidal state. Hypnotic suggestions are, therefore, unique to the interaction between patient, condition and symptoms or affects, and must be created with attention to detail to ensure that they will be accessible and acceptable to the person receiving them. The use of specific language is a very important factor in making suggestions acceptable and accessible to the patient.

Once the hypnotic state has been induced, this state can then be used for positive suggestions to be introduced to the patient. Suggestions must be made with a single objective in mind, and, whenever possible, should be given to the patient using positive vocabulary. This is discussed in more depth in Chapter 7 on hypnotic language patterns. These types of suggestions are known as post-hypnotic suggestions, and are the suggestions which the patient is instructed to carry out after termination of the session. These form the hypnotherapeutic component of a hypnosis session.

Hypnosis cannot turn a patient into something which they are not, nor can it give anyone the ability to do something that they could not do before. There are (as yet unsubstantiated) claims of individuals undergoing hypnosis to display the capacity to communicate spontaneously in a language of which they had no prior knowledge (known as 'xenoglossy'). Under examination these cases have often demonstrated that the patient is speaking the words but has little or no understanding of what they are saying. In some instances the individual has later recalled having seen these words written down, or heard them spoken in a context which they had previously forgotten.

Clinical hypnosis does, however, provide five fundamentals that then enhance the patient's capacity to enhance what is already present. It can do the following.

Amplify abilities

The relaxed and focused state of awareness experienced in hypnosis allows patients to remember positive events, and successful memories, therefore reminding them what they are already capable of doing once they put their mind to it, that is, focus.

Focus attention on whatever task is in hand in order to achieve it more easily

As the hypnotic state is one of concentrated attention, where distractions are reduced, and a relaxed and focused state is suggested, individuals can put all of their attention to achieving their objective. The installation of positive suggestions in hypnosis reduces individuals' capacity to talk themselves out of their objective by giving conflicting auto-suggestions.

Help create a specific goal so the mind can work towards it

The pre-induction talk between patient and practitioner will refine the objective of therapy. Other, potentially conflicting objectives are compartmentalised to reduce distraction. Objectives are subjected to SMART principals to reduce loopholes.

Reduce stress or anxiety

Poor stress coping strategies or over-anxiety will often result in a mental paralysis, which, in turn, holds patients back from gaining a therapeutic benefit. By being taught self-hypnosis the patient can learn to manage stress better, learn how to relax and reduce unnecessary nervous tension or anxiety.

Stimulate autonomic functions

In order to be prepared for a future event, the autonomic nervous system will become activated in advance, as in the fight or flight response to stress, or salivation when imagining a feast. Through the intense physical experiences associated with clinical hypnosis individuals can be prepared for a future event, and, as they are preparing in a focused and relaxed state, will be able to optimise their experience of the event when it happens.

The form and content that suggestions will take come from the pre-induction talk between the practitioner and the patient. Only one suggestion at a time can be processed fully, so time is taken to clarify the patient's objective in each session. The patient will only accept suggestions of a positive nature. Milton Erickson conducted studies on this phenomenon and concluded that if inappropriate suggestions were made to a patient the patient would discriminate, fail to respond and even construct methods of retaliation for the breach of trust.

If suggestions are made to *not* do something, it can often produce a reverse effect. An example of this would be to try to not think of a white horse. Immediately, this produces the effect of thinking about a white horse. This is a direct result of the way in which the brain functions. In order to not think of something it has to be thought of first. This event is fundamental to the way in which suggestions are delivered in clinical hypnosis. In hypnosis the suggestions relate to what patients want, not what they don't want. Clear and direct instructions are given to focus patients' attention away from their problem, or patients' experience of a positive state is used to create a different approach to their problem. The practitioner will direct the patient to think differently about their problem, based on strategies the patient may have previously employed, and by doing so, encourage them to behave and respond in a more appropriate manner.

There are occasions when negative states are recalled in hypnosis as a way of reminding patients that they only know they are in pain if they have a memory of what having relief from pain means to them. There are times when these useful, that is, non-pain-based, memories may have been made inaccessible, and hypnotherapeutic techniques can be used to work on stimulating those memories to produce a healthier response or more control over the pain state.

There is another form of suggestion given in hypnosis, known as 'ego-strengthening' suggestions. They will be included in most sessions. Once again, this type of suggestion works because it is an extension of everyday life. It is natural to feel better when told we are looking well, or particularly trim, today. Conversely, when we are told that we do not look well, the focus of attention shifts towards noticing every ache and pain. Ego-strengthening suggestions encourage patients to look for positives around and within them, and generally enhance their capacity to experience positive states. The suggestions will also move the emphasis away from self-monitoring and on to an appreciation of what is going on around them as a way of encouraging patients to take their mind off their symptoms.

Suggestions take one of two forms.

Post-hypnotic suggestions

These relate specifically to the presenting condition and will direct the patient's attention on to specific thoughts, feelings or actions. Post-hypnotic suggestions will be created by the clinical hypnosis practitioner and will be based on the language patterns, past successes of the patient and specific objective of the process.

Ego-strengthening suggestions

These are included in most clinical hypnosis sessions except where contraindicated by the condition. The purpose of ego-strengthening suggestions is to remind patients of events and successes where they have achieved their objectives. The purpose of this is to remind them what they are capable of. The primary purpose of these suggestions is to act as a motivational tool with regard to their condition, and encourage patients to recall positive states so that they will feel better generally.

How does clinical hypnosis work?

At the moment no-one fully comprehends how clinical hypnosis works. This is partly attributed to an attitude held by some practitioners, who hold a firm belief that standard protocols cannot be created, that most of the work done in a consulting room is unique to the individual practising it. This attitude does not lend itself to double-blind trials, and, therefore, there is a dearth of *good* research on the subject. Medical practice will not fully accept a procedure for general application that cannot prove itself a reliable approach with a predictable outcome. The other reason for a lack of definitive evidence on how clinical hypnosis works has been the result of the ways in which success has been evaluated. Much of the research that has been done has relied on subjective evaluation from the patient. This is necessarily open to interpretation. However, this situation is changing with a shift towards objective testing of variables such as basal skin temperature, heart rate and, most significantly, brain function during the hypnotic state. It appears that the breakthroughs in technology with MRI scanning and brain mapping will finally put clinical hypnosis on the neurological map, and, it is hoped, move it towards the mainstream of medical application.

Part of a clinical hypnosis session will include describing to the patient a model of the way in which clinical hypnosis will work. The key point to be aware of here is that the process can be explained and described in a number of ways. The significance of explaining it to the patient lies in creating a model of the event that will best help them experience the benefits of the process. One of the models most commonly used describes the differing areas of the brain and its functionality. Patients will often complain that they do not understand how hypnosis can do something that they cannot do for themselves. This model describes the event of hypnosis as an opening up of the neurological pathways between conscious thought processing and unconscious activity and function. The result of this is that the individual can then gain access to the information they need to successfully make the changes they require.

Using the functionality model gives patients an explanation of why hypnosis will work, and, just as significantly, why they have not been able to make the changes for themselves before. Although this is still a model in as far as it cannot yet be fully endorsed by the facts, it does appear to be one of the more accurate explanations of how hypnosis operates on the brain, and it seems that medical science is starting to back up this model as the mapping of brain function continues to enhance our knowledge and understanding of differing brain events. There are a number of other models which can be used to describe hypnosis to the patient, depending on the mindset of the patient and the nature of the condition. It really depends on the character of the patient, the nature of the condition and the expectations of the process, as to which model can best be used. How to select the appropriate model is discussed at length later in this book.

Explaining the events of hypnosis and the potential applications of clinical hypnosis is only one element in how it works. Another key element in the modern use of clinical hypnosis in a medical setting is the concept of the therapeutic partnership. To put this concept into context it is worthwhile looking at some of the history of hypnosis. To understand where it exists today, clinical hypnosis needs to be viewed as a product of the society within which it is conducted.

Before the First World War, some physicians considered hypnosis to be an event that was a side-effect of hysteria, and, as only women were capable of suffering from hysteria, only women were capable of experiencing hypnosis. This changed when soldiers returned from the trenches after the First World War with symptoms of hysteria. Hysterical symptoms were reclassified, and hypnotherapeutic techniques were then used to help soldiers suffering from what would later become known as post-traumatic stress disorder.

In Freud's day, when he observed Pierre Janet using hypnotic techniques with patients, hypnosis involved the patient being told what to do and carrying out the suggestion unquestioningly. Milton Erickson, the most well-known exponent of clinical hypnosis in modern times, would hold what seemed like a gentle, rambling monologue with his patients while he made indirect suggestions to direct the patient's attention to various aspects of their condition. He believed that 'confusion was the gateway to learning', and by helping the patient to produce questions, they would then be able to come to their own conclusions about how best to help themselves.

From these examples we can observe that one of the factors in how clinical hypnosis operates relates to the interaction between the practitioner and the patient. This is at least partly based on expectation and a clearly defined relationship between the two parties. In modern clinical hypnosis, the practitioner defines the process as one in which both the practitioner and the patient are active participants in the event and in deciding on a therapeutic outcome. We move in more rapid times than ever before, and clinical hypnosis is moving towards defining itself as a brief strategic therapy, whereby the patient will only attend for a small number of sessions (interspersed in some instances by homework by the patient). Clinical hypnosis is now much more clear and streamlined as the therapeutic partnership defines specific parameters required to produce changes in the patient's state and perception of events. These parameters are discussed in more depth in Chapter 7, 'Creating the hypnotherapeutic protocol'. This development lends itself to clearly defined protocols, which can then be submitted to research. There will always be practitioners who believe that the work they do is unique to their talents as an individual. To a greater or lesser degree this might be true, as the more competent and confident practitioners will create a greater degree of trust and rapport with their patients. Without it, the initial induction of hypnosis does not easily occur, and therapeutic suggestions will not be readily received.

As to the process of hypnosis itself, this works by the more easily observable processes of physical relaxation allied with mental focus. In this state patients will be relaxed and focused, and can therefore more easily access capabilities of which they were previously unaware, or thought to be outside their conscious control. Induction of hypnosis is done by means of specific suggestions relating to focus, for example by instructing patients to pay attention to their breathing, and is enhanced by suggestions of relaxation and focused attention. The practitioner may make suggestions for patients to notice their breathing becoming deeper, or becoming less aware of noises around them. Once a patient is observed to be in a relaxed and focused state, their altered awareness is enhanced by a process known as 'deepening', whereby any observable phenomena are commented upon, and amplified by the practitioner, by use of verbal cues or suggestions, or by changing their own breathing patterns. Patients will then reach a level of hypnosis where they feel comfortable and relaxed, and suggestions for changes in thought, activity or emotional states can be made. Although the process is usually a linear one, with the hypnotic suggestions for change following suggestions made for inducing and deepening the hypnotic state, there are some techniques when suggestions are interspersed.

The procedure of clinical hypnosis takes into account:

- patients' personality
- their personal history
- history of the presenting condition
- the specific objective for the session.

A treatment appropriate to the patient can then be formulated by using the above criteria. Each session is different and personal, and it is vital that patients experiencing the clinical hypnosis are aware that this process will take them to the positive limits of their potential, physically, mentally or emotionally, whichever combination of personal characteristics they need to use to fulfil their goals. How this is achieved is discussed in more detail in later chapters.

Another model to describe the process of hypnosis is a very simplistic one. This is to describe hypnosis as a state of focused concentration with associated physical relaxation. As this is such a familiar state, and the suggestions made can seem obvious, patients may be curious as to what is different in the hypnotic experience from, for example, making these suggestions in the form of affirmations. To amplify this model, the practitioner may then go on to explain hypnosis in terms of where the brain experiences various events. The cortex (in this model being equated with conscious or logical thought) already knows what the patient needs to do to make a required change. However, the limbic system (here equated to memory storage and the autonomic nervous system) stores memories on habits and unconscious processes. Hypnosis can be described (as in the previous model) as a mediator between these two areas of the brain, allowing the conscious process to rest, whilst the unconscious areas receive and interpret the information, allowing changes to take place.

As to the specifics of how hypnosis works with any one patient, there is as yet insufficient research into the topic, and we will only get a clearer picture when comprehension of the neurological processing increases.

- Clinical hypnosis is an extension of natural states of awareness.
- It cannot make anyone do or be something that they are not already capable of, although it can help to focus on developing skills and resources already present.
- Suggestions made in hypnosis will only be taken on board by patients if they feel safe and comfortable.

Chapter 2

Self-hypnosis

There are some theories of hypnosis that state all hypnosis is self-hypnosis. To a certain degree there is some accuracy in this as no person can be hypnotised against their will, so an element of the process is complicity or agreement in undergoing hypnosis. However, there is a reported difference between the experiences of self-hypnosis as opposed to hetero-hypnosis, which is done by one individual (an operator) to another (the subject). When individuals do self-hypnosis, they take themselves into a focused state by using their awareness as the operator. They then make suggestions to influence or access their own unconscious processes and events such as memories, effectively hypnotising their unconscious mind as the subject, while still remaining conscious and able to make suggestions as the operator. Individuals who have experienced both hetero- and self-hypnosis will often describe the self-hypnosis as less intense, or they find it more difficult to relax as fully as if they were experiencing the same suggestions made by another person. The advantage of self-hypnosis over het-ero-hypnosis is that the individual may feel more able to fully control the experi-ence, and can also practise it and gain benefit whenever they need to. They can also improve their ability to experience the phenomena of hypnosis and will therefore respond more fully when hypnotised by another person.

The best way to learn self-hypnosis is to be taught it whilst in a hypnotic state. This way individuals learn the process on both a cognitive level, so they can repeat the procedure, and on a physical level, where they experience the event as it is being described to them. In this way, subjects will be able to both control the event and recognise the phenomena that indicate they are hypnotised when they later come to practise for themselves.

Teaching a patient self-hypnosis has a number of benefits. It gives the patient a new, and potentially more appropriate, coping strategy for dealing with their condition, it is a method of relaxation for patients who say they do not know how to relax, and it is a framework for continuing therapeutic and beneficial suggestions which patients themselves can control. In addition, the number of formal sessions required can be reduced by incorporating suggestions made by the patient in self-hypnosis.

By learning self-hypnosis patients can benefit in terms of their general health and wellbeing, as well as in terms of their presenting symptoms. Additionally, the more frequently patients experience hypnoidal states, the more comfortable they become with them. Although there is no direct correlation between the depth of hypnotic state experienced by patients and their capacity to benefit from the therapy, it is appropriate to suggest that when a patient is at their most relaxed, they are more inclined to take on board suggestions which they might otherwise reject by analysing in more detail.

This chapter contains the script of the companion CD. If you wish, you can use this as a template to teach patients self-hypnosis. You can read from the script, modulating your voice in a similar way to that on the CD, whilst using the pauses (denoted by the ellipsis (…) between phrases), to observe the patient. If you are intending to do this, it is important that you read the whole volume first, as the script is only one component in a hypnotherapeutic session. If your intention is purely to teach self-hypnosis to your patient you will still need to observe the six stages of the hypnosis session described elsewhere in this book. Attempting to hypnotise a patient 'cold' will rarely work.

If you do intend to teach patients self-hypnosis, you will need to make them aware of the following benefits. The practitioner does not need to discuss all of them with a patient, only the ones which are most relevant. If you try to hypnotise a patient without fully explaining the potential benefits for them, the motivation levels will be much lower than if you do explain the benefits. In this way we are also introducing the concept of suggestions and motivation for change even before beginning the formal hypnosis process. This element is also explored in more depth in Chapter 3, 'The structure of a clinical hypnosis session'.

What are the benefits to the patient?

The most effective method of motivating the patient to do self-hypnosis is to sell the benefits.

Stress management

When an individual responds to a stress-inducing situation, the body will activate the autonomic nervous system. This is split into the sympathetic and para-sympathetic systems. The sympathetic nervous system is responsible for producing biochemical and physiological changes to prepare the individual to respond to that stressor. This response is known as 'fight or flight'. Once this response has been discharged, the para-sympathetic nervous system kicks in to reset the biochemistry and physiology back to resting mode. This circuit is known as the 'stress cycle'. Individuals who have started to respond poorly to stress will find that their ability to activate the para-sympathetic nervous system is reduced. The result of this is a system which remains on high alert. Self-hypnosis promotes these para-sympathetic nervous system responses. Self-hypnosis is a relaxed state, and is therefore also an excellent way of reducing stress, allowing the patient to complete the stress cycle safely and promote more effective ways of responding to stress.

Distraction technique

As with many of the techniques used most effectively in hypnosis, the use of self-hypnosis as a distraction technique is an extension of a natural process. If you look on the faces of people travelling in a train, for example, they will absorb themselves in music, reading or by watching the landscape passing by. Within this framework, self-hypnosis is used as a state of absorption to take the individual away from their immediate surroundings. The benefit of using self-hypnosis is once again its accessibility, and the fact that whilst in hypnosis, the individual is able to experience hallucinatory states whereby they can alter their perception of the event around them.

This ability to alter the sensory experience is especially useful for patients in physical pain or undergoing surgical procedures. In this situation self-hypnosis can be used as a method of distracting attention away from the immediate environment, whilst producing specific alterations in perception to reduce awareness of pain, or alter it into a different sensory experience. Once pain management has been taught by a practitioner, patients will be encouraged to reinforce this state on a regular basis. Studies have taken place which suggest that if hypno-anaesthesia is induced by a practitioner and then reinforced by the patient every four hours during a normal day, for a three-day period, the efficacy of the anaesthetic effect will be twice that of those who only had the initial session.

Personal enhancement tool

In the self-hypnosis script, patients are encouraged to focus on positive events. Patients with low self-esteem are more focused on the negative aspects of any presenting condition, so patients are encouraged to use the self-hypnosis to give themselves positive suggestions. The self-hypnosis script states that 'positive, beneficial suggestions can be made' and that 'negative suggestions, or suggestions which would be of any harm to you, will not be accepted by the unconscious part of your mind'. The emphasis here is to get patients to begin to be more aware of auto-suggestions of a negative nature, which they may have already been making in relation to their condition, such as 'I don't think I will get better'. The direct suggestions in the self-hypnosis script instruct the patient to start thinking more positively. This concept is known as 'ego-strengthening' and is a characteristic of most hypnosis scripts except where contraindicated by the condition, for example depression.

Improved control

One of the elements of patient care to be aware of is the aspect of perceived loss of control resultant from presenting condition, medication or medical procedures. This is particularly relevant for chronic conditions. Self-hypnosis is completely structured and controlled by the patient.

Patients cannot overdose on self-hypnosis, and they can self-medicate, allowing them to choose when, where and how much benefit they can gain. This is why it is so vital to fully explain what hypnosis is, and what benefits patients might reasonably expect from its use.

Self-hypnosis can also be referred to as 'self-induced relaxation' (SIR), a term coined by Michael Joseph, founder and principal of the London College of

Clinical Hypnosis. The change in terminology from self-hypnosis to self-induced relaxation is made to give patients an enhanced perception of control over the event, as, for some patients, the mention of hypnosis is sufficient to increase their anxiety levels rather than reduce them. The script used on the CD refers to self-induced relaxation throughout.

In addition to an explanation of the benefits, if you are intending to teach patients self-hypnosis you would still need to take them through the six stages of the hypnosis session. As there may be no specific condition the patient wishes to deal with, the emphasis in the session will be placed on the benefits of learning self-hypnosis. The benefits then become the therapeutic outcome component of the session. The six stages of the hypnosis session are discussed comprehensively in a later chapter.

The practitioner would need to explain to the patient how to prepare for self-hypnosis, including the significance of setting a time. This way, when patients do enter hypnosis they are setting themselves up for a positive experience of the event.

Preparing for self-hypnosis

Before undertaking self-hypnosis certain preparations are necessary. The practitioner will instruct the patient to go through the following process before starting to make suggestions to enter a hypnotic state.

Set a time

Decide how long to spend in the hypnotic state. It is better to start with around 10 minutes, and then increase the time. Aim for approximately 20 minutes as an optimum. The time is to be set internally, rather than with an external alarm. This encourages patients to start trusting their capacity to control internal states. The accuracy with which they achieve this time can be a useful calibrating device. If patients are easily able to assess the time they have set for their self-hypnosis, it can be judged that they are generally functioning healthily. If patients wake before the time they have set, it is often an indicator of stress. Conversely, when patients' assessment of the time in the hypnotic state is longer, it can be an indicator of lack of motivation or lethargy. It is a possibility that when an individual is in a hypnotic state they unconsciously use their heart rate as a device for calculating time. If they are stressed, the heart is beating faster and therefore their concept of time will be that it is faster than real time. If the patient is dejected or lethargic, this effect is reversed.

Find a time and place to be undisturbed

It is important that the practitioner explains that if there is a need for patients to become fully alert as their attention is required elsewhere, they will be able to immediately bring themselves back to a fully alert state.

Sit down or lie down

It is generally recommended that patients do self-hypnosis in a comfortable reclined chair rather than prone. This is because there is an association of sleep with lying down. If the self-hypnosis is to be done immediately before sleep, then the patient will obviously be lying down and then fall into a natural sleep where they will wake at the appropriate time.

Assume a neutral position

The patient is then instructed to arrange the body in a neutral posture, with arms resting on the lap or at their side, feet uncrossed. This is demonstrated as the posture patients are in when being hypnotised to learn self-hypnosis. A neutral posture is preferable to ensure that no distractions are caused by paraesthesia. Additionally, other postures, such as crossed arms and legs, can be counter-productive as they may be associated with tension or stress.

Close the eyes

The patient is then instructed to close the eyes to start the self-hypnosis suggestions. Eye closure alone becomes an auto-suggestion to become more internally aware, and to begin to pay more attention to thoughts and, in this case, suggestions. Patients should also be informed that if they wish or need to open their eyes at any point during the process they will be able to do so.

During the process

The patient is directed to be aware that sounds and sensations will be perceived throughout. These should not distract them, and they can treat them as background to their auto-suggestions. If a sound or sensation requires the patient's immediate attention, they can deal with it, and, should full alertness be necessary, the self-hypnosis will end immediately and they will be fully aware.

Positive suggestions

People will often have more than one objective for self-hypnosis. Unless the self-hypnosis has been taught so that the patient can supplement suggestions made during a formal hypnotherapeutic session, it is best to keep the suggestions as individual concepts, positively phrased. The most important aspect is that only suggestions of one kind should be made at any one time. Examples of useful suggestions for self-hypnosis are suggestions of focus, relaxation, confidence or motivation. The suggestions need to be phrased by the patient to refer to the near future, rather than the present. The rationale behind this is explained in greater depth in a later chapter. Patients are encouraged to continue making these suggestions in self-hypnosis until they have achieved the objective. Only then is it appropriate to start on new suggestions. The aim of this is to build up a conditioned response to the suggestions in order to begin to respond unconsciously to them.

Waking up

The self-hypnosis script gives instructions on how to wake from the hypnotic state. If sleep results from the self-hypnosis, that is natural and patients need to be assured that if this happens, they will wake from their sleep as normal.

The hypnotic voice

When inducing a hypnotic state, the practitioner will modulate the voice to be appropriate with the words spoken. You can listen to the CD to identify how the voice changes depending on what is being said, and at what stage of the script. When delivering a hypnotic script, the voice is used to maintain the interest of the subject, and to place particular emphasis on certain instructions or concepts.

Delivering a script

The instructions from this stage to the hypnosis script itself are relevant to most types of hypnotherapeutic sessions. Variations are discussed more fully in Chapter 7, 'Creating the hypnotherapeutic protocol', as is the construction of therapeutic suggestions.

> - Phase of hypnosis: Induction and deepener
> - Change in voice quality: Slow, gentle, quiet
>
> The purpose of the voice slowing down, and becoming quieter and increasingly gentle, is for the patient to begin to focus their attention on what is being said. The quality of the voice needs to be sufficiently interesting for the subject to begin to tune in to the spoken words. If subjects need almost to strain to hear they will pay closer attention, whereas if the voice is dull or kept at a normal sound level, subjects can let their attention wander.

> - Phase of hypnosis: Therapeutic suggestions
> - Change in voice quality: Dependent on therapeutic approach and condition
>
> If the approach is authoritarian, the voice may be raised slightly when making suggestions. When making permissive suggestions the voice

remains gentle, but is made more persuasive in tone. There may be times when suggestions are made more rapidly. This is useful with individuals who are analytical or have secondary gains in relation to letting go of a problem. These individuals often attempt to deconstruct the suggestions. The change in pace reduces their capacity to analyse all the suggestions, so some of them will slip past their analytical guard and be taken on board.

- Phase of hypnosis: Ego-strengthening
- Change in voice quality: Motivational, directive

These suggestions are sometimes interspersed throughout a script. In this instance, the way in which the suggestions are delivered will be congruent with the stage of the script in which it is delivered. In formal hypnotherapeutic scripts, the ego-strengthening suggestions come just before the awakening suggestions and their purpose is to remind the patient of positive states, and encourage them to stay focused. The direct suggestions can be emphasised with a change in tone, pitch and volume of the voice accordingly.

- Phase of hypnosis: Awakening
- Change in voice quality: Louder, faster, more directive

The voice in hypnosis is soothing, and modulation should be gradual. Care must be taken to ensure that the voice has a non-sexual quality. Keeping the words spoken precise and clear, especially when at the state of therapeutic suggestions ensures this. The speed, pitch and volume of the voice by the end of the awakening process should be almost that of normal speech. It should never be louder as the aim is to bring patients back to a state of normal alertness at a natural pace so that when they are fully re-oriented they will then feel normal.

Use of the pause

In scripts, there are pre-set pauses, usually denoted by '...'. In these pauses, the practitioner needs to observe the patient and take note of the following.

- Has the patient followed any instruction made?
- Is the patient showing any signs of distress, such as speeding up of breathing rate?
- Are any of the suggestions being particularly well-received?

The practitioner can then vary the script by either repeating an instruction, in the first instance, or by modifying the forms of suggestion to alleviate the distress, in the second instance.

In the introduction, deepening, therapeutic suggestion and ego-strengthening stages of the script the pauses can be timed by silently and mentally repeating the phrase just spoken – twice. By doing this, the practitioner will have sufficient time to observe the patient, whilst giving the patient time to process the suggestions given.

When awakening the patient, the pause can be reduced to one silent repetition of the phrase just spoken. As the practitioner becomes more proficient at suggestions, pacing with patients' breathing patterns will become more natural.

Delivery of suggestions

The practitioner may wish to deliver specific ego-strengthening suggestions to patients when teaching them self-hypnosis. Suggestions are most effectively delivered once the patient has been told that they will soon be awakened. It is considered that at this point the patient will go more deeply into hypnosis as their confidence to experience the state is at its height. Suggestions can be delivered as follows:

'. in a few moments' time … I am going to wake you … but BEFORE I wake you … I am going to make a few simple, positive suggestions … suggestions which will be able to help you … '

At this point deliver the suggestions discussed with the patient during the pre-induction talk. Always use positive language, suggesting to the patient something they wish to work towards, rather than away from, for example suggestions to 'sleep deeply and well' rather than 'not stay awake worrying all night'. As you can see, explicit in the latter statement is the very suggestion the patient wishes to avoid (stay awake all night and worry).

Use of self-hypnosis for the practitioner

Battle fatigue or burn-out can be a common factor with any individual who works in a one-on-one scenario with individuals who have problems. Self-hypnosis is a useful method of dealing with this potential problem. Additional to this, a calm, relaxed practitioner of clinical hypnosis will inspire more confidence and be able to build quicker rapport than one who is tense and anxious. Self-hypnosis is recommended as a tool for practitioners to use on a regular basis to reduce their own stress levels. When seeing patients on a regular basis, self-hypnosis can be used as a way of releasing any tension induced by the sessions themselves. It can also be used as a way of preparing for future sessions. It really comes into its own as a stress management tool when practitioners are in a situation whereby they do not have anyone with whom they can offload. In the self-hypnosis, the practitioner can access a healthy mindset for working with each patient and ensure that any issues relating to them can be filed safely, and then processed unconsciously.

Script for use with patients

The accompanying CD contains an audio recording of this script. Listen to the CD first before attempting to deliver the script yourself.

Self-induced relaxation

First ... gently allow your eyelids to close ... and with your eyes comfortably closed ... you can find that ... you can allow your eyelids to remain comfortably closed ... and you can start to become aware of your breathing ... your chest rising and falling ... and ... as you do ... the most important thing for you to know is ... that you are in control of this process ... and will only go as deeply into this focused state ... as you feel comfortable to go ... and ... if at any point during this process you need to be fully awake and alert you will be ... and ... when you have learned how to take yourself into this focused state of awareness ... you will be even more in control ... as each time you practise ... you become more relaxed ... and can trust that part of your mind which already knows how to focus inwardly ... to keep you completely safe ...

Allow your mind to pay close attention to your breathing ... your chest rising and falling ... that you no longer need to be aware of your body at all ... as you already trust this part of your mind to be awake even when you are asleep ... to regulate all those unconscious processes ... the things which you do not even need to be aware of and they happen ... and ... in a few moments' time ... when I teach you how to take yourself into this focused state ... you will find ... that progressively ... you will be able to take yourself into this state ... without even being aware that you can do this ...

In a few seconds' time ... you will hear me count down from ten to one ... and with each descending number ... between ten and one ... you are going to become one-tenth more relaxed ... ten per cent more relaxed ... with each descending number ... each descending number ... will help you to go ... one-tenth deeper ... into that wonderful ... focused state of concentration ... that in any event ... will become deeper and deeper ... as we go on ... if ... while I am counting ... you would experience a slight ... though very pleasant ... physical sensation ... as if you were floating ... floating down ... that will be fine ... it only means that you are drifting ... into an ever-deepening state ... of physical as well as mental state of relaxation ... that will become deeper ... and deeper ... as we go on ...

So, ready ... ten ... nine ... and deeper and deeper ... eight ... seven ... six ... drifting down ... ever deeper relaxed ... five ... four ... three ... and deeper and deeper still ... two ... one ... and all the way deep down focused and relaxed ...

The easiest way to learn how you can take yourself into a focused state of relaxation ... is to first experience this focused state ... and I will remain silent for a few moments while you FULLY EXPERIENCE THIS FOCUSED STATE ... [Pause]

And now ... I am going to teach you ... how you ... all by yourself ... can re-enter into this wonderfully relaxed state ... all you have to do is to ... find the time and the place where you can ... be comfortable ... and have a reasonable chance of being undisturbed ... you then make yourself comfortable ... you can sit down or lie down ... as long as you are comfortable ... you then gently allow your eyelids to close ... and with your eyes comfortably closed ... you begin ... silently and mentally ... to count down from ten to one ... you count slowly ... at the same rate as you breath out ... or even at every second out-breath ... and with each descending number ... between ten and one ... you are going to become ... one-tenth more relaxed ... ten per cent more relaxed ... with each descending number ... each descending number ... will help you to ... go one-tenth deeper ... into a state of focused concentration ... and this state of focused concentration ... will become deeper and deeper ... as you practise ... and when you reach number one ... you will be as deeply relaxed ... in as deep a state of physical relaxation ... as you are now ... in fact ... you might go much deeper ... because each time you practise ... you become more proficient ... and each time ... you go deeper relaxed than before ... and you can stay in this relaxed state for as long as you like ... now ... to come back into full conscious alertness ... all you have to do ... is to silently ... mentally count up from one to ten ... and with each number ... you come a little more ... back into full conscious alertness ... and by the count of ten ... your eyes have opened ... and you are back into full conscious alertness ... feeling fine ... wide awake and fully refreshed ... ready to cope better ... with anything ... anybody ... and any situation you have to handle in your daily life ... feeling more confident ... and a little more optimistic too ... than you have felt before ...

Now ... every time you practise your self-induced relaxation ... you will find that ... as each day goes by ... you are going to become ... and will remain ... a little more mentally calm each day ... your mind becomes clearer and clearer ... crystal clear ... physically ... you become more relaxed too ... and as a result ... you will be able to think more clearly ... see things more clearly ... so that nothing ... and no-one ... will ever be able to worry you ... or upset you in quite the same way ... you will feel more relaxed about yourself ... more relaxed about the world around you ... it will be perfectly natural ... that you will enjoy so much greater self-control ... over the way you think ... over the way you feel ... over the way you do things ... and over the way you respond ... to any stressful situation ... you encounter in your daily life ... many of those things ... people and situations that once used to stress you ... will no longer stress you at all ... you will be able to identify ... many of those stressful situations over which you have no control ... so you stop wasting nervous energy ... about the things you cannot change ...

And now ... I am going to bring you back into full conscious alertness ... I am going to count from one to ten ... and with each number ... you will slowly begin to come back into full conscious alertness ... you will open your eyes by the count of ten ... and you will feel fine ... refreshed ... fully wide awake by the count of ten ... you may open your eyes at any time you choose ... every part of you will be back here with me in full conscious alertness ... by the count of ten ... so, ready ... one ... two ... three ... coming back to full conscious alertness ... four ... five ... six ... seven ... more and more alert now ... eight ... nine ... ten ... open your eyes ... open your eyes ... fully alert now ... feeling fine ... wide awake and refreshed ...

The above script is courtesy of Michael Joseph
Founder and principal of the London College of Clinical Hypnosis

Chapter 3

The structure of a clinical hypnosis session

There are six stages to a clinical hypnosis session: introduction, induction, deepening, post-hypnotic (therapeutic suggestions), the awakening stage and the final stage is post-hypnosis, which consists of feedback and debriefing the patient.

Introduction

The introduction session takes the form of a discussion between patient and practitioner. It is a structured discussion that includes a number of components, each with a specific objective. It is important to remember that patients need to be clear on each of these components before they will be secure to enter a hypnotic state. It is further worth noting that failure to incorporate each of these components before taking the patient into hypnosis can often adversely affect their experience of the state, and of the therapeutic objective.

The stages within the introduction section can be equated to the five-stage Calgary–Cambridge model of the medical consultation. Within this familiar structure, the specific use of language described in this volume takes the concept one step further. These skills then become portable into any diagnostic setting where the emphasis of the communication is on accuracy and speed.

Patients also need time to look around the room, to accommodate sounds and the sights, or even unaccustomed smells of the room in which the hypnosis is going to take place. On the subject of smells, it is best to keep the room where the hypnotherapeutic session will be as smell-neutral (odour-free; odourless?) as possible. Smells are very evocative of memories, and can often be distracting for the patient. Once patients have had time to become accustomed to their surroundings, and if they are disturbed when in hypnosis, they will be more comfortable to stay in the hypnotic state as they became familiar with their surroundings before the hypnosis started.

There is no hypnosis as such during this stage, but the elements of the hypnotic state can already be introduced at this time. Patients will become more relaxed, more focused and progressively directed towards solutions and positive states – just as will happen when they experience the hypnosis. Done properly, this section is a precursor to the hypnotic state, as well as an opportunity to re-assure patients and collect sufficient information for them to have a positive experience of hypnosis, as well as a successful therapeutic outcome.

Information gathering

In the introduction to this stage the practitioner will follow a fixed sequence of questioning. First, the presenting condition is initially pin-pointed briefly. This is kept to a minimum. Once the patient is more com-fortable, later on in the session, the following specifics of the condition are then discussed:

- what it is
- how it developed
- symptoms
- physical and psychological impact
- ways in which hypnosis may help.

Information about the patient as an individual is then requested

This is then used in hypnotic script formation and will include details such as personality or resource states, current anxieties or potential stressors, any future anxieties of the patient with regard to potential change, and sensory future pro-jection which can be incorporated into visualisations.

More time and emphasis is placed on the patient rather than the condition to initiate perceptual changes. It is said that a good physician will tell a patient what many things about themselves that are functioning correctly before moving on to the problem – in this way the emphasis is on the positive.

A clear and realistic outcome for treatment is established

This is a vital component for the effective use of clinical hypnosis. Once a clear and realistic outcome can be established, the practical methodology of using clinical hypnosis to achieve this outcome can be constructed – by both the patient and the practitioner.

Case history

A full history of the condition and a description of the symptoms are then taken. The purpose of this information-gathering stage is manifold. It is to establish to patients that they are not the problem, and that the condition does not occur all the time, and that often there was a time before the condition occurred, or at least before it affected them as severely. This process begins to deconstruct the problem both qualitatively and quantitatively (that is, it does not happen all the time, and there are times when the symptoms are less pronounced, and even possibly a time when it did not exist). A comprehensive description of the type of questions necessary to establish an appropriate case history can be found in Chapter 7, 'Creating the hypnotherapeutic protocol'.

The following is an outline of appropriate information to include in the case history. It is important to be aware that the case history is not intended as a comprehensive medical or personal history.

It is essential that information requested from patients must be of specific value to the session. If patients feel that they are being asked for information that they do not feel is relevant, rapport will be lost and, in the worst case scenario, this will create anxiety. It is important to remember that one of the fears of hypnosis which patients might have is that of being compelled to give out information about themselves. It is therefore vital for the practitioner to know why they are asking the questions so they can respond appropriately if asked by a patient to justify the need for certain information.

The requirement for information requested during the case history section of the session comes under one or some of the following groupings. Each of these will be discussed to ensure that practitioners knows why they are asking the questions. This will allow each practitioner flexibility with their questioning technique, provided the required information is collected. The information provided by the patient will be then used in the following.

Creating the hypnotic script

The way in which patients talk about how they experience themselves, the world around them and their interaction with the problem will give the practitioner indicators as to the type of language and suggestions to make during the script.

First, this will personalise the hypnotic experience to the patient's current experience of the world. The second purpose is to use patients' language, cognition and behavioural patterns – the way they talk, think and act, as an indicator of how the suggestions can best be delivered.

Allowing patients to gain a greater understanding of their potential

One of the underlying themes of clinical hypnosis as a therapeutic tool is that patients who created a problem for themselves will necessarily know how to solve that problem, even if they are not consciously aware of that solution. Appropriate questions in the case history will be phrased in such a way as to lead patients to think about their solutions, rather than their problem. Questions are therefore best phrased in positive language and will be solution-focused.

Discovering how the patient developed this condition

The practitioner will ask questions relating to the history of the condition, that is, when it started, when it developed from being a condition to being problematic for that person, and what was going on in their life at that time. A timeline of the condition can then be established and any times at which the condition was more or less manageable can be identified. If a patient believes the condition has been present all of their life, this will also be an indicator of possible courses of action for treatment.

Analysing how patients currently manage their condition

Questions are asked relating to how the condition currently affects the patient are asked during this section. So symptoms are described, and the patient is encouraged to give as full a description of the event as possible. This series of questions will be used to identify what, if anything, currently helps them to manage the condition. This information will also give the practitioner an indicator as to whether the patient is currently motivated.

Understanding the interaction between patients and their environments as a result of this condition

The present ego-state of the patient is assessed in this sequence of questions in order to identify, first, whether the patient is ready for the implications of change, and, second, if the patient has thought through the ways in which this change will affect their life. If any secondary gains for the symptom are present it will become evident at this point when the patient begins to justify their current behaviour and moves the focus of the process away from making changes.

Creating a safe environment for patients to express their concerns

The case history needs to be more than a question-and-answer session; it is an opportunity for patients to become more comfortable with the practitioner, to assess the practitioner's level of skills, and also for patients to start to feel that the practitioner is gaining a clear picture of them and their problem. The case history is also an opportunity for the practitioner to begin to lead the patient, with open-ended questions, to come to their own conclusions as to what is most appropriate for them in terms of therapeutic objectives.

Producing a safe and realistic outcome

By the end of the case history component, the practitioner and the patient will have agreed on an appropriate course of action for the patient to take with regard to their condition. It may seem like a very obvious point to raise at this stage, but patients frequently come for hypnotherapy knowing what they do *not* want, that is, their condition, but have not thought through what they *do* want, that is, their objective. The outcome must be put into clear terms by the practitioner, and agreed upon by the patient at this stage. The potential number of sessions required to achieve this outcome is then clarified. It is important to note that in the modern use of clinical hypnosis the objective is as few sessions as possible, supplemented if necessary with homework by the patient.

Rapport

Establishing rapport is a vital component of the introduction section. Without it the patient is not going to be able to enter a state of hypnosis. One of the easiest ways to establish rapport is by encouraging patients to talk about themselves rather than the problem. Within this structure, the following information is also identified:

- What do you do to relax?
- What do you enjoy/did you enjoy doing?
- What would you like to enjoy?
- What will you be doing when you no longer have the problem?
- What do you want specifically in relation to the problem?

Discuss the hypnosis state

Identify any previous experience

It is important to be aware if patients have had previous experience of hypnosis and to discover what, if anything, they found useful about the process. The methods used, if well-received by the patient at the time, can be replicated. If, on the other hand, the patient did not like a particular method, this should be avoided.

Allay fears and misconceptions based on that experience

If a patient has been hypnotised before, it is always useful for the practitioner to ask questions about the patient's experience of the phenomena of hypnosis. If they did not 'feel' hypnotised, it is often that a misconception was not discussed in sufficient depth. An example would be if a patient stated that they did not feel hypnotised because they could hear everything that was said to them. The practitioner can then explain that hearing everything in hypnosis is to be expected; in fact, it is important that they do so.

Patients with no previous experience of hypnosis

In this situation, this fact will need to be considered when discussing the hypnotic state, so that any of the patient's concerns can be addressed appropriately. Often, a fear of dominance or loss of control will be a concern of the patient new to hypnotic experiences, or their pre-conceptions are based purely on impressions drawn from the media.

In summary, the practitioner should include:

- what the patient expects of the experience
- an explanation and description of the events of hypnosis
- and incorporate any fears or misconceptions at this stage.

Back to the problem

By this time the patient will feel considerably more relaxed and will be more comfortable to discuss their condition. There are rare occasions when patients will change direction at this point and tell the practitioner that they would rather deal with some other problem, rather than the condition with which they originally presented. If this is the case, the patient is demonstrating that they have thought through their condition and also that they feel the practitioner has understood them and they feel sufficiently comfortable to deal with a different matter which the patient has decided will be of more value to them.

The patient will do most of the talking during this section, with the practitioner directing them to remain focused on the aspects of the condition that are relevant when creating the hypnotic script, and evaluating the most appropriate objective, protocol and treatment plan.

Any questions before we start the clinical hypnosis?

At this point, if the previous sections have been covered comprehensively, the patient should have no questions as the practitioner should have already gone through all the relevant information. By asking patients if they have any questions it gives them time to consider anything that may have occurred to them during the introduction session, and to prepare mentally. Giving patients a specific opportunity to ask questions is done at this stage as by this point patients will be more comfortable than at any previous point in the session. If this question was asked at the beginning of the session, it is unlikely to provoke any response as patients are usually too anxious, too polite or have not thought of any questions about the session by then. Once this question has been asked, and all responses dealt with, the patient then should be able to enter hypnosis with a positive and motivated mindset. Patients' questions are covered in Chapter 4, 'Questions patients ask', which gives an indication of the wide range of questions that may be asked and the type of answers that are appropriate.

A practical point

Before commencing hypnosis, and after the introduction session, patients should be asked if they wish to use the toilet. Nothing distracts a patient more than a full bladder!

Before taking a patient into an induction, the practitioner will lead with statements to encourage the patient into hypnosis. An example of this could be: 'When you are ready to let go of this problem, you can … start to relax … .'

Suggestions for induction of hypnosis will follow from this point. Once again, specific phraseology is used to encourage patients into hypnosis, with their focus on positive events of the future. This phraseology is created from an amalgam of the language the patient uses, alongside solution-focused phrases which direct the patient towards their therapeutic objective. The other aspect of this phraseology comes from the patient's interaction with their condition. The introduction part of the session can take anything up to 45 minutes.

Induction

This is the part of the session in which the practitioner usually asks patient to close their eyes in order to concentrate their attention on sound or physical feelings. An induction encourages a state of internal focus, whilst external distractions are reduced or limited. The induction can be carried out in a number of ways (visual, auditory or kinaesthetic, or a combination thereof), depending on the patient's responses to questions in the introduction section.

The most effective methods of inducing hypnosis involve utilising the modes in which the patient already relaxes. By recalling the memories of these relaxed states, patients will begin to remember the physical state of relaxation and this will in turn amplify their potential to experience the hypnotic state. Broadly put, the practitioner will take note of which sense the patient involves in past-relaxed states, and will use this sense as a guide for ways of taking them into hypnosis. For example, if a patient states that they listen to music to relax, auditory stimulation is used. Conversely, if a patient swims for relaxation, a technique using physical (kinaesthetic) stimulation is utilised. The only occasions when these relaxation states would not be used to assist in recalling a certain state would be if the patient uses 'false friends' to relax, such as drink, drugs or smoking. Each one of these events is contraindicated to a positive experience of relaxation and is often harmful to the patient. Out of interest, if a patient does use these methods of relaxing, it is an indicator of poor coping strategies to stress and this may also need to be dealt with as part of the therapeutic process.

> All inductions involve fixation of attention at some level where the patient is then focused upon one specific location, sense or idea. The purpose of a formal induction is eye closure.

Visual inductions

Visual inductions involve suggestions for focusing the eyes on one specific location or paying attention to the muscles of the eyes. An example of this would be where a practitioner asks the patient to focus on a spot upon the ceiling, and notice eye fatigue. If the patient has any eye impairment, glaucoma for example, a visual induction may be contraindicated. If the patient's condition has eye problems as a symptom of the presenting condition, for example migraines, visual inductions should not be used.

Auditory inductions

Auditory inductions involve suggestions to stimulate the auditory cortex. An example would be when the practitioner asks the patient to listen to the sound of their voice. In auditory inductions patients are directed additionally to deselect other sounds around them so they become part of the background. Another way of increasing internal focus in an auditory manner is to ask the patient to focus on internal, rhythmic sounds, such as breathing or a relaxed heartbeat.

Kinaesthetic inductions

Kinaesthetic inductions involve suggestions to stimulate the physical sensations or feelings. An example of a kinaesthetic induction would be when suggestions of hand levitation are made, inducing a physical dissociation. Other examples include asking patients to focus on experiencing warmth or feeling their muscles become progressively limper. In each of these examples the feelings are associated with sleep or relaxation.

Authoritarian versus permissive

In the delivery of suggestions, there are two other main variations in the ways in which induction can be achieved and these can fit into any of the above categories.

The first approach to be discussed is that of authoritarian presentation, in which suggestions are made in a directive, commanding manner. The advantage of this type of approach lies in its rapidity. The disadvantage is that, should the patient fail to comply with the suggestion, the rapport established in the pre-induction section of the session is eroded. This method is favoured for patients who already have a mindset of accepting suggestions unquestioningly, whether as a result of their career choice or temperament, or the severity of their condition. It is worth remembering that those patients who are used to issuing orders and having others comply with them also respond better to this way of presenting suggestions. In extreme cases, such as emergency circumstances, authoritarian suggestions are favoured over permissive suggestions as they are thought to capitalise on the freezing reflex that occurs before the response of 'fight or flight'. In the instance of hypnosis being induced at this moment, a rapid dissociation away from the experience of the immediate surroundings occurs. Similarly, use of direct suggestions can be seen from the work of Dr Patterson at the University of Washington Burns Centre, who developed a virtual reality programme to suggest that patients are flying around a snow-filled canyon whilst dressings are being changed.

The second approach involves the use of permissive suggestions. These are requests and invitations rather than orders. They involve repetition and presentation of ideas in gentler terms. This type of approach is favoured for those patients who are anxious, for younger patients and those who are experiencing hypnosis for the first time, as it allows them more apparent control over the process. The advantage of this approach is that it gives the practitioner more time to calibrate patient response. The possible disadvantage is that patients may become so relaxed that they sleep before therapeutic suggestions can be made. Permissive suggestions will take longer for the changes to take effect, as repetition and invitation involves allowing the patient to analyse the suggestions before taking them on board and so there will be a longer period of time between suggestion and response.

Deepening

This is the section of the script where the patient is taken deeper into this focused state of relaxation, or into a heightened state of internal awareness. The patient is asked to continue focusing on physical changes, such as breathing becoming deeper, or the experience of dissociation from immediate surroundings that takes place. The patient becomes progressively more aware of unconscious processes and functions, theoretically producing a corresponding change in the brain whereby the brain centres involved in apparently unconscious thought and activity also become more active. When this takes place, and suggestions for change at this level are made, then the patient is more likely to be able to take control over these thoughts and activities which were unconscious, and therefore inaccessible, at a more conscious level.

The practitioner aims to take the patient into as deep as state of hypnosis as possible. Calibration of when this has taken place is made by observing changes in the patient's physiology. When the state stabilises, and after suggestions are made for waking, post-hypnotic suggestions are made to the patient. Also known as 'therapeutic suggestions', these are the suggestions for positive changes which are to take place after termination of the session.

Therapeutic suggestions (post-hypnotic suggestions)

These need to be:

- phrased positively
- relating to one subject at a time
- achievable
- realistic.

As mentioned already, suggestions must be of a positive nature. It has been observed that the brain receives suggestions more efficiently when made in sets of three, so if you are doing self-hypnosis, try to find three different ways of making the same suggestions. For example, to give your auto-suggestions to feel more calm generally, you could phrase this in the following ways: 'I can be more relaxed … more able to deal with any situation … more in control of my own responses'. In this way the mind can select whichever is most appropriate to gain the outcome of being calm, no matter what the situation.

These post-hypnotic suggestions are made most effectively after patients are told that they will be woken from the hypnotic state. This is for a number of reasons: the patient may be enjoying the relaxed state and therefore relax a little more, or, in some cases, the patient may experience relief that they have not been given any suggestions to change and can therefore continue to operate within the status quo. Once told they are to be woken up, patients will go to their optimum depth of hypnotic state. Whatever the reason, the patient is more receptive at this point and suggestions based upon the discussion in the introduction section are made. Only suggestions previously agreed upon are made, and these should be made wherever possible using the patients own words and language patterns.

Ego-strengthening suggestions

These are suggestions for general physical and emotional health and wellbeing, and are interspersed with the therapeutic suggestions for the awakening. These suggestions are based around patient history ('You can feel as happy as you did when you passed your driving test ... ') and positive future scenarios ('You can look forward to enjoying life now that you no longer smoke ... ').

Ego-strengthening can be a therapeutic process in itself, for example in confidence building. Here the post-hypnotic suggestions would involve the patient focusing on feeling confident and relaxed in future scenarios. The additional aim of ego-strengthening is to assist patients to think in a positive manner generally, and therefore to be able to apply this mindset to the specific problem they have been experiencing. Ego-strengthening is not suitable to all conditions or patients as the suggestions it involves may be unrealistic to the patient because of their current mindset (for example, reactive depression).

The primary purpose of ego-strengthening is to act as motivational fuel to encourage the patient to carry out the post-hypnotic suggestions.

Awakening

The purpose of awakening is to bring the patient to full conscious alertness with hyperamnesia of any suggestions that need to be carried out post-hypnotically. During this process, any suggestions that have been made explicitly for the purpose of the hypnosis, such as limb heaviness or tiredness, are removed. Suggestions for general health and wellbeing are also made at this stage. A signal, such as counting, is usually given before the awakening process to prepare the patient to be brought out of the hypnotic state.

Post-hypnosis

At this point the patient is given an opportunity to ask further questions, and this includes the practitioner answering any questions that may have arisen as a result of the patient's experience of the hypnotic state. This reassures patients that they remained in control throughout the process, and any feedback can be used for future sessions to tailor suggestions more effectively. After the debriefing process, the practitioner can then reinforce any suggestions made during hypnosis and encourage patients to observe any changes occurring in themselves.

When the session is used to teach self-hypnosis, at this point the patient should be encouraged to practise the technique whilst with the practitioner. This allows patients to feel safe, and demonstrate that suggestions made in the hypnotic state were fully understood.

Some practitioners suggest to their patients that they should not discuss the process with anyone else during the following 24 hours. This is to encourage the unconscious processing of the hypnotic event during their sleep. Amnesia of the specifics of the hypnotic state is more likely to occur when these suggestions are adhered to.

Homework

Once the formal therapeutic element of the session has been concluded, the patient may be instructed to do homework. Homework is the name given to specific tasks, thought processes or behaviours which the patient is directed to action after leaving the session. This may include practising self-hypnosis. If self-hypnosis has been suggested, the practitioner should reinforce the process at this stage, reminding the patient of how to do the self-hypnosis.

For activities relating to the patient's interaction with their condition, the practitioner will repeat the suggestions made as part of the formal hypnosis session, unless amnesia has been used to induce a deliberate 'forgetting' of the suggestions. This might be used for patients who smoked to say to themself 'I have no desire to smoke' and to distract themselves deliberately when in a situation where they used to smoke, or for a phobic patient to press the tip of the thumb and first finger together to produce relaxation in a specific situation.

The purpose of homework is to reinforce therapeutic suggestions, and also to break the associated patterns of thought, feelings or actions which were associated with the condition.

Future sessions

When patients are clear on what is expected of them after the session, dates for any future sessions (if necessary) are then set. The timing between sessions is dictated by the condition and the speed at which patients respond. Some conditions will need reinforcement as soon as possible, whereas others will need time for the changes to be accepted and acted upon before continuing with the therapeutic sessions. This is discussed in Chapter 7, 'Creating the hypnotherapeutic protocol'.

Chapter 4

Questions patients ask

During a clinical hypnosis session, patients are given an opportunity to ask questions. Questions asked by patients at the start of the session will vary to those asked just before the practitioner takes them into hypnosis. The difference in these questions relates to the fact that patients will feel more comfortable and relaxed, and will ask more detailed questions about hypnosis further into the session than at the beginning of the session when they are unsure of quite what is going to happen. A competent practitioner recognises that most patients new to hypnosis will have similar concerns and questions, but will wait until the patient asks them.

This chapter provides examples of the types of questions often asked by patients, and discusses appropriate responses to them. It is valid to bear in mind that patients will ask questions as a way of uncovering the specific answer to a question, but also as a way of measuring the practitioner's knowledge and competency. A question poorly answered can break rapport. There is also a danger in answering a question too comprehensively. The practitioner must always keep a balance between education and information.

The purpose of answering patients' questions is, therefore, twofold. First, to reassure patients and therefore reduce their anxiety and second, as a means of setting up the patient to safely receive suggestions whilst in hypnosis. An appropriate answer to a patient's question in this context is one that reassures the patient and informs them of what to expect in terms of their future experiences, whilst still remaining within the framework of a clinical hypnosis session. As a result, some of the answers are linguistic models tailored to patients' concerns about the process rather than 'correct' or definitive answers.

Is hypnosis an altered state?

There are non-state theorists, such as Dr Graham Wagstaff (1981) of the University of Liverpool, who have conducted studies that demonstrate that events experienced during hypnosis can also be replicated out of this state. The conclusions drawn are that hypnosis is not a unique altered state, especially as events reported by those supposedly experiencing hypnosis have varied substantially. It is a discussion that will be ongoing until in-depth research based on objective, rather than subjective or experiential criteria has been undertaken.

Current developments in MRI and PET scans mean that we now have a much clearer picture of the neurological event during differing events, such as waking, sleeping and hypnosis. Results show that there is a distinct alteration in brain activity during the induction of hypnotic states, and also during the time when suggestions are being processed. Further research is still required to define which specific areas participate in enhancing receptivity to suggestion.

How will I know that it has worked?

Patients will sometimes ask what happens if it didn't work. There are a number of reasons for this question, one reason being that the hypnosis itself was not sufficiently explained to the patient. Another reason for this type of question may be that the patient has general feelings of negativity and their focus of attention remains on their problem rather than on the therapeutic outcome. If this question comes up the practitioner will repeat some of the suggestions made whilst the patient was in hypnosis to move their focus of attention to the benefits of change. The patient is also directed to actively look for the differences between how they were before the session, and what has changed after the session. The terms 'change' or 'differences' are used rather than emphasising the benefits, as the patient will be more able to notice these effects in a non-judgemental manner. If the situation arises whereby patients inform the practitioner that they did not gain the benefit which they expected, a further session refining specific suggestions and enhancing the patients' capacity to focus on the benefits by the use of ego-strengthening suggestions will then be given.

What can hypnosis do for me that I could not already do for myself?

This is a key question in motivating patients to experience hypnosis, and also in their ability to gain benefit from the therapeutic suggestions. Some patients may have had their condition for such a long period of time that they believe there is no other way for them to be – an example of this would be the migraine sufferer who has no recollection of a time when they did not suffer from their condition. There are others who feel that the situation they are trying to change is such a part of their lives they could not imagine themselves without their behaviour. Smokers often fit into this category. In either case the explanation of the advantages of using hypnosis will incorporate information on the ways in which the brain best receives suggestions, as well as informing the patient of how the hypnoidal state can help. It will be explained to the patient that there is a major difference between the type of auto-suggestions given out of hypnosis, and suggestions given by a practitioner while the patient is in hypnosis. This difference is what makes the hypnosis more effective. While individuals are focused mentally and relaxed physically they are more able to receive suggestions that in a full waking state they may reject, or talk themselves out of. The other element here relates to brain function and it can be simply explained to patients that when you are in hypnosis, the areas of the brain which relate to controlling responses will be activated and accessible to conscious control. This way patients will be able to make the changes necessary. Hypnosis effectively acts as a mediator or translator between conscious control and unconscious function, allowing patients to more easily and effectively make the changes.

Is hypnosis different from meditation?

Hypnosis and meditation can be very similar in the way in which they are experienced physically, and with some forms of meditation, mentally. The main difference is in the specific mental processing which takes place in hypnosis as a result of suggestions. There are some forms of meditation that use guided imagery, and this can also be used in hypnosis, although in hypnosis this usually takes the form of a specific therapeutic metaphor. When an individual is meditating, the emphasis is often on achieving a specific internal state whilst in meditation; in hypnosis the primary emphasis is on achieving external changes after the hypnosis session is completed. According to studies by Paul Ekman at the University of California, San Francisco Medical Center, meditation, like hypnosis, activates the left pre-frontal lobe which is linked to positive emotions, self-control and happiness, and also influence the amygdala, which is effectively the alarm centre of the brain, therefore reducing the potentially harmful effects of stress. Therefore, hypnosis can be experienced as basically similar to, or basically different from, meditation, depending on the individual's mind-set and previous knowledge of either process.

Is clinical hypnosis like stage hypnosis?

For some patients, their fears of hypnosis are based on what they may have seen in a stage show. Their fears often relate to the idea of losing control, or being influenced inappropriately. If this question comes up, the practitioner will need to explain that there are many different events going on in a stage show, be able to differentiate between that and what goes on in a clinical hypnosis session and what patients believe they have seen on stage.

It can be explained to patients that there are a number of components to a stage hypnosis show. The first of these is expectation. When people go to a stage show they already know what to expect of the event, and will therefore already be predicting what they are going to experience. The next process is peer pressure. It is very rare for people to go alone to a stage show; they usually go in groups. Within each group there will be one or two individuals who are more exhibitionistic by nature, and the rest of the group will encourage them to getting up on stage. Frequently, people will drink alcohol before arriving at the stage show, and this will encourage the potential participants even further as their inhibitions are lowered.

Once the audience arrives at the stage show, there will be a preselection process to discover those who will end up on stage. This usually involves suggestibility tests. The purpose of these tests is not to find the most easily hypnotisable subjects, but to find the exhibitionists. One example of these types of test is the 'hand clasp test', where members of the audience are instructed to hold their arms straight out in front of them at shoulder height, and to interlink their fingers and press their palms together. Suggestions are then made that at a given cue, they will be unable to pull their hands apart. Suggestions are then given returning all sensations to normal. Once this has been done, the audience watchers who are placed around the auditorium will pick out the people who drew attention to themselves by indicating that they could open their hands, and therefore were not hypnotised. These people will often raise their hands up in the air to draw more attention to this fact. These people are then selected to come up on stage.

Once up on stage, the hypnotist encourages the people on stage by directing the all the applause of the audience to the person 'being hypnotised', and by directing them to more and more outrageous behaviour. The final component in the show will be the abrogation of responsibility, whereby a person on stage can do all manner of things whilst claiming the stage hypnotist 'made them do it'. Some stage hypnotists encourage their audience participants to more outrageous behaviour by telling them that the more they do, the more intelligent or good fun they are, so they work on the ego of their subject. When the person comes off stage they can tell their friends that they do not remember what they have done, or they were under the influence of the stage hypnotist – so there can be no 'blame' attached to their behaviour. Frequently, the participants in a stage show will be given some free tickets to a future performance. In the meantime, those who went to the show will tell those to whom they give the tickets all that happened, and the stories will become progressively more outrageous. By the time the next group goes to the show they are already heavily primed for the event, and the exhibitionist of the new group will want to outdo the first performance – so it goes on.

A hypnotised individual would not be a good performer in a stage show as when a person is in hypnosis they hardly move, and any responses shown will be slow and small. Patients asking about stage hypnosis can therefore be assured that during clinical hypnosis they will become relaxed and quite still, will only do what they feel comfortable to do and will remain in control throughout.

There are instances when people who participate in stage hypnosis shows are genuinely in an altered state (other than that induced by alcohol). This could happen if the participant is a somnambulist or is vulnerable to suggestions as a result of a pre-existing condition or sequence of events, or because they want to believe themselves to be hypnotised, and begin to enter a hypnotic type state as a result of this belief. Following the sudden death of her daughter, Sharron Tabarn, after she had participated in a stage hypnosis show, Margaret Harper formed the campaign against stage hypnosis (CASH). The aim of this organisation is to get stage hypnosis banned in the UK.

As with any type of questions that patients may ask, the key is to tailor the reply in response to their concerns, rather than attempting to give a comprehensive answer. Patients who ask about stage hypnosis usually want reassurance that they will be safe and in control.

Are patients in control of the hypnotic event and can they exercise free will over accepting the suggestions?

Suggestions made in hypnosis will reflect the discussion between patient and practitioner during the pre-induction talk. Suggestions for the purpose of creating and maintaining the hypnotic state, or for the purpose of therapeutic benefit, are based on the pre-induction discussion only. As soon as they enter hypnosis patients will then engage their conscious awareness to analyse what has been said to ensure that they feel safe and comfortable with the suggestions being made. They will bring themselves out of hypnosis if they are not comfortable with the suggestions, or if new suggestions are introduced. Even at the somnambulistic level of hypnosis, patients remain in control and would respond to suggestions with an awareness of their personal safety still intact. If the practitioner asked patients to do anything that they did not feel safe and comfortable with, or made suggestions which were outside the framework already discussed in the pre-induction talk, patients would bring themselves out of hypnosis.

No-one can be forced or encouraged to do something that they would not already be inclined to do. The ability to reject suggestions is enhanced by the focused state of attention pivotal to the experience of hypnosis. It therefore follows that anyone in hypnosis will be able to reject or accept suggestions in the same way as they would in a normal state. However, the capacity to act upon positive suggestions is enhanced by this state of physical relaxation and focused concentration.

Can anyone get stuck in hypnosis?

This type of question is another that relates to patients' concerns over how much control they have over the experience. The easiest way to reassure patients in this situation is to inform them that they control the experience throughout. Another aspect of this concern is what would happen to them if something distracts, disturbs or in some way incapacitates the practitioner before they bring a patient to full conscious alertness. Patients asking this type of question need to be reassured that they would, in this circumstance, bring themselves out of the hypnotic state. It may take a little longer for full re-orientation to occur, as part of the 'waking up' procedure includes returning all sensations to normal. However, the patient will be normal and fully alert after a short while.

Can a patient be made to forget what has happened?

Remembering and forgetting events, as well as restructuring them, is all part of memory codification. A patient in hypnosis will remember everything that is of value for them to remember, and can give themselves permission to 'forget' (a more appropriate term would be 'neglect to remember') anything which is causing them disturbance. As with the issue of control, patients can be reassured that no other person can force them to forget, but that forgetting is sometimes part of a natural process for healing and change, and that if it is appropriate for them to forget about something which concerned them, then they may choose to do so. In this way, clinical hypnosis is described as working in a similar way to the natural process of memory.

When a patient experiences an abreaction in hypnosis and needs an explanation of why it happened

An 'abreaction' is an emotional response, triggered by a memory or state. This is experienced while the patient is in hypnosis and can often disturb or upset the patient – often because it was unexpected. On awakening it is important to reassure the patient that the experience was an appropriate one and give them time to discuss it, should they so require. Abreactions can be described to the patient as an emotional discharge that, as they were not able to experience the emotion at the time of the original disturbing event, needed to be experienced, for example being told as a child not to cry. Now they have done so there is no further requirement for the symptom. Occasionally, abreactions are spontaneous, with no apparent origin. The main emphasis here is to assure patients that the abreaction was natural and appropriate, and that they can now move forward.

Management of the patient during an abreaction is discussed fully in Chapter 7, 'Creating the hypnotherapeutic protocol'.

Patients view their capacity to enter hypnosis as an issue of willpower

Hypnosis is *not* about the practitioner exercising their willpower over that of the patient. It is appropriate to inform patients that they require willpower to experience hypnosis, and that they will only experience the state depending on how much willpower they have. The hypnotic state can be then described as one that gives the patient *increased* levels of willpower over their own thoughts, behaviours and emotions.

Patients who recall memories whilst in hypnosis

Patients who approach their condition analytically often benefit from experiencing events in hypnosis that could then give them a rationale for their behaviours, thoughts or feelings. If a therapeutic process involving evocation of memories is to be utilised it is vital to inform patients of the malleable quality of memory – and to assure them that the event may not be 'real' in the way that they are experiencing it and that this memory is only their current perception of an event, real or imagined, designed to assist them in making a beneficial change in their lives.

Some patients are afraid that they will recall events which they would rather not remember, or of which they have little or no recollection – memories which they have deliberately chosen to forget consciously. If a patient does re-experience a memory of this kind, the emphasis in the therapy is on the patient permitting the recalled information to allow them to move forward. The practitioner will always emphasise that any memory recalled in hypnosis may not be a strict representation of the actual event, and as a result is only their current perception of the event. As a perception it can be understood and worked through. If a patient has spontaneous recall of a memory of which they had no previous conscious awareness, the practitioner will explain that this has happened only because they feel safe to allow it to happen, and because this memory has some relevance on their current situation.

Patients who expect hypnosis to be similar to a general anaesthetic

If patients expect to be completely unaware of their surroundings and the internal experience during hypnosis, on being reawakened they may feel that they were not hypnotised. Before inducing hypnosis the practitioner needs to describe the state in such a way that patients will understand their experience of the event as it occurs. One possible description is to talk of the hypnotic state as being similar to that of sleep on the physical level (so they can move around if they want to, but they may experience sensations of limb heaviness and tiredness), whilst the mental processes are in a state of heightened focus whereby they hear and can analyse everything as it is suggested to them. In this situation the explanation must also include the suggestion that it is important for this mental awareness and processing to continue as patients will need to be aware of the suggestions so they can decide which are most appropriate to take on board. It can also be explained that as patients enter deeper levels of hypnosis there may be times when their awareness of their surroundings will vary in intensity.

Patients who do not believe they can be hypnotised

If a patient has this mindset, it is usually based on preconceptions of hypnosis as a form of mind control. Patients can be assured that they will only be hypnotised if they wish to be hypnotised, and that it is a naturally occurring state which they have experienced before, such as when driving along a familiar road or absorbed in a piece of music. After the hypnosis session it can be useful to ask patients how long they believe they have had their eyes closed. The majority experience the time as being considerably shorter than it actually was. This, in turn, acts as a convincer that the hypnotic event was different from simple eye closure.

Patients who are unsure about their potential to experience results

If patients question whether hypnosis will work for them, the practitioner can first explain that hypnosis works with their personality to enhance the positive aspects that are already in place. During the hypnosis session, suggestions are made to direct patients' attention on to positive changes in the future. Practitioners can reinforce these suggestions in the post-hypnotic section by suggesting that patients look for any 'differences' in the way they are experiencing life events.

Patients who believe they are asleep during hypnosis

If a patient does fall asleep during hypnosis, this can be easily recognised as there will be more movement, and changes in breathing patterns will occur. A patient in hypnosis is generally quite still, whereas someone who is sleeping will make irregular and jerky movements, change their position, and the breathing can become louder and quite stentorian.

Some patients, however, go so deeply into hypnosis there are times when they do not register everything being said. This occurs when they are fully comfortable with what is being said, and raising no conscious objections, allow themselves to go deeper into the hypnotic state than they expected. When this is the situation, the practitioner will explain this to them and reassure them that everything which is of significance for them to remember will be recalled. The key question to differentiate between those who felt asleep, and those who actually went to sleep, is whether they responded to the awakening script. The practitioner will then highlight this as an indicator that they were in hypnosis rather than actually sleeping, because if they were truly asleep they would not respond.

Patients who believe hypnosis may conflict with their religious beliefs

Some patients are concerned about suggestions made because of religious considerations. As with most questions asked, this is the result of concerns about mind control, or fears that suggestions made by another person might in some way contradict their belief structure. If this is an issue it is essential that the practitioner finds out the nature of these concerns. Once this is done, an explanation of how the process of clinical hypnosis helps individuals to take more control of themselves is made. Reassurance is also given that it is not about another person gaining influence over them. This can be amplified if appropriate with the suggestion that their faith will be secure throughout and can even help them experience the therapeutic effects of the session at an even more profound level.

There are some events that occur in charismatic churches whereby an individual enters an altered state on a given cue or trigger from a central figure. The individual may experience an abreaction, such as crying or shaking, and in some instances, gain specific benefit from the experience. If a patient comes along who has seen this event occur and believes that hypnosis is something similar, it is vital to explain the parallels, and the differences. The parallels are in the aspects of expectation and trust in the other individual (in this case the preacher or healer), and the differences are in that in charismatic healing the benefits gained are attributed to the power of God, in clinical hypnosis they are attributed to the individual themselves. For patients with a religious framework, emphasis will be made of the fact that no-one can be forced to do anything outside their moral, social or religious beliefs in any form. To further reassure patients with this mindset, the practitioner can take useful parts of their belief system to create a motivational scenario. By describing clinical hypnosis in a way that reinforces the positive aspects of patients' belief systems, the practitioner can utilise patients' beliefs to strengthen the suggestions for change.

Patients who expect a 'cure' from hypnosis

There are patients who have completely unrealistic expectations of clinical hypnosis. They believe that, once hypnotised, they will be completely 'cured' of their condition. The first point to make here is that the term 'cure' is not used within this framework. Cure implies total and permanent remission from all symptoms. Patients who talk of cures will often be those who believe hypnosis is something that is done *to* them, rather than them being an active participant in the event. They will often describe their expectations of the process as one where they hear, feel and remember nothing until they are woken up, and at that point they are symptom-free. These types of individuals may have this belief structure as a result of expectations from the media or stage hypnosis, or because they do not wish to take any responsibility for operating their symptom as they have a secondary gain to maintain.

In any event, the practitioner will need to emphasise to this type of patient that the process is a therapeutic partnership, in which they need to take an active role. It is further emphasised that it is, in fact, essential for patients to hear, feel and remember during the process so that they only take on board suggestions that are safe and comfortable for them. The final element in the explanation creates flexibility into the outcome, so that patients are allowed to notice the changes as they take place, so they become natural to them, rather than waking up from the hypnosis with a totally new way of behaving installed in them. This would feel unnatural and would very soon be rejected. In this way, the unrealistic expectations are broken down and reconstructed into a sequence of statements that will allow patients to experience hypnosis as a relaxed and pleasant state, and therefore gain positive effects from the suggestions.

Patients who believe they cannot be hypnotised because they are too analytical, intellectual or intelligent

Analytical, intellectual or intelligent individuals often have as part of their characteristic make-up a tendency to believe that no-one can hypnotise them, as they often believe hypnosis to be some kind of trick or mind-game. This attitude stems from a commonly held, but now very outdated, belief that only those with weak will can be hypnotised. In this circumstance, a patient will be told that the more analytical/intellectual/intelligent they are, the deeper into hypnosis they will be able to go. To go further, the practitioner will actively encourage the patient to continue to apply this characteristic all the way through the hypnotic state. The other element here – of fear of losing control or being tricked – is also overcome by the practitioner actively promoting their analytical/intellectual/intelligent character trait as part of them taking control of their experience of hypnosis, and exercising choice over the suggestions they decide to accept.

Patients who believe hypnosis to be potentially dangerous

There are those who have as part of their preconceptions the idea that hypnosis is in some way dangerous, that they could get stuck, or that the hypnotherapist could make suggestions to them which would be harmful or make them give out personal information which they would not otherwise disclose. Anxious patients may focus on apocryphal stories of hypnosis sessions where patients were subjected to unpleasant experiences and were subsequently traumatised. To reassure patients that this is not the case, the practitioner will often point out that any individual for whom hypnosis could potentially be dangerous *cannot* be hypnotised, that it is a self-defence mechanism. Anyone able to experience hypnosis will be able to control the experience throughout, hear all suggestions that are made, and will therefore be able to filter out any suggestions potentially harmful to them. It is also appropriate to mention that if patients do not have these fears dealt with appropriately, they will remain in an anxiety state and will then be unable to enter hypnosis properly.

Patients who believe that hypnosis will help them experience past lives

The popular press has much to answer for with regard to past life regression. Whenever there is a newspaper article or programme about this subject, people will contact hypnosis practitioners with view to experiencing a past life. There are a number of issues which need to be dealt with here. First, clinical hypnosis is not something to be experienced purely for experimentation. Second, if an individual wishes to gain some therapeutic benefit from the process, there may be other methods that would be more appropriate. To ensure that those people with genuine need are assisted in the best possible way, the practitioner will ask a series of evaluation questions before the pre-induction talk to clarify the reasons for wanting past-life regression rather than any other specific protocol. These evaluation processes are discussed in later chapters. It is worthwhile noting that there are a number of religions which have past lives as part of their structure and therefore its potential therapeutic value for these individuals is a recognisable one.

Patients who come for clinical hypnosis to perfect their neuroses

There are some individuals for whom the specific benefits of retaining their symptoms are greater than those to be gained from getting better. These secondary gains will often create behaviours by the patient to maintain the symptoms. These strategies can often include the patient attempting many different ways of gaining remission, from medication to therapeutic approaches, and in some extreme cases, unnecessary surgery. This allows the patient to maintain the symptom whilst still appearing to attempt ways of improving their situation. The mindset of these types of patient will prevent them from being open to any type of suggestions that could assist them to make the appropriate changes to get better. They will then be able to continue to maintain their symptoms on the basis that they are 'trying everything, but nothing is working for them'. With this type of patient there are a number of directions that can be taken. One way is for the practitioner to do ego-strengthening rather than approaching the condition per se, with a view to encouraging the patient to find better ways of coping. Another way would be to encourage them to look into the future, and begin to imagine how life could be for them without their condition. Either way, it is not appropriate to attempt to deal directly with the symptoms of their condition before the mindset of the patient has been changed to a more positive one.

Patients who do not want the therapeutic outcome

There are occasions when individuals come along for clinical hypnosis, but do not want to be there. This may because, as in the case above, they have secondary gains that are keeping them in their problem state, or it may be a situation where the motivation is not theirs. This occurs when, for example, a partner, or a GP books a patient in for smoking cessation, but the patient themselves has little or no motivation. If this is the situation, the practitioner can look to use the hypnosis to change the patient's mindset, or to do the session anyway – emphasising the positives of change. In clinical hypnosis motivation plays a key role in the recognition and acceptance of change and patient suggestibility. It is a good idea for the practitioner to speak to the patient before they come for the session to be able to preassess whether hypnosis is going to be appropriate for them. Whenever another person phones in to make a session booking on the patient's behalf it is a fairly good indicator that their focus of attention is not on the session. As a result, a seasoned clinical hypnosis practitioner will insist on speaking to the patient before their session to avoid the situation of a poorly motivated patient arriving in the consulting room.

Reference

Wagstaff GF (1981) Hypnosis, Compliance, and Belief. St Martin's Press. New York.

Chapter 5

Hypnotic events, application and contraindications

Before discussing the patient experiences that can occur as part of the hypnotic state, it is necessary to identify the indicators of 'levels' or 'depths' of hypnotic state that can be experienced. Although there are no clearly defined delimiters between levels of hypnosis, there are a number of visible and experiential indicators which can be observed. Not all patients will experience all hypnotic events, nor will they necessarily experience different levels. Each patient will experience the event in varying ways, depending on the following:

- **Personal history.** Patients who have had experience of hypnosis before, or who have experience of meditation states, will often be more comfortable and notice more of the phenomena taking place in hypnosis. Patients who are generally stable and have a strong ego state will have fewer concerns about suggestions being made, and will therefore exercise more free will when responding. This in turn allows them to experience deeper states than patients who are not so comfortable with themselves. If patients are highly motivated to achieve the therapeutic outcome this will influence their receptivity to suggestions. It is important to note that there are individuals who come for clinical hypnosis as a last resort and want the hypnosis to work for them so much that this counters their ability to enter a hypnoidal state. They are so anxious for success that this anxiety prevents them from focusing and relaxing sufficiently to enter hypnosis.
- **The condition.** If the condition has symptoms of anxiety or patients have issues about control, these can make it more difficult for patients to experience relaxed states. Most conditions, whether physical or psychological in origin, will worsen with stress, and the more stressed the individual, the longer it will usually take to induce hypnosis. This is why it is so important to reassure patients that they dictate the level of hypnoidal state which they will experience, and of the fact that they remain in control throughout the event. Patients will go to a level of hypnosis at which they feel most comfortable. At this level they will experience the optimum relaxed state from where they will be able to experience the therapeutic components of the hypnosis. When they reach this level they will remain there until they have gained sufficient insight into their condition, or received the unconscious signals which they need to move forward. Suggestions for change are most often made in the hypnosis script immediately after patients are told that they will soon be woken up. It is generally held that this is the most effective

level at which to make suggestions as patients will often hold back from achieving their deepest potential of hypnotic state through fear of letting go, or anxieties about change.

- **The content and delivery method of suggestions given by the practitioner.** The content and delivery of suggestions are directly influenced by the patient's way of operating and viewing the world. Suggestions are created from this worldview, and enhanced by the practitioner feeding back in hypnosis the type and form of language which patients use to describe their symptoms and the outcome they require. If the content of the suggestions is appropriate to the patient's interaction with their condition, they will continue to achieve progressively deeper levels of hypnosis. This happens as they become comfortable and familiar with more of the hypnotic phenomena with each session. The result of this is that their capacity to enter hypnosis increases with increasing levels of experience until they plateau at their optimum potential depth. If the method used by the practitioner to deliver the suggestions is one that the patient is comfortable with (for example, the chief executive officer of an organisation being given direct authoritarian suggestions), the levels of hypnotic state being experienced can also increase for the patient.

- **The level of rapport established with the practitioner.** The practitioner needs to demonstrate three main attributes: competence, an understanding of patients and their conditions, and the ability to create clear objectives for the therapy with patients. In the first area, that of competence, this is demonstrated by a confident and open approach, and the ability to communicate with patients in their own language. Understanding comes from listening and interpretation skills, allowing patients to *feel* that they are being listened to and that the practitioner demonstrates empathy where appropriate. The final point, creating clear objectives for therapy, involves all of the skills described above, whereby the practitioner takes what patients present, and with them, creates a clear and specific objective for therapy which will be achievable and acceptable to them. Rapport skills can be learnt, but as each experience of working with a patient will be unique, it is worth noting that when this process is done well, it is invisible to the patient.

Juxtaposition of suggestions

Throughout the various levels, a skilled practitioner of hypnosis will introduce suggestions that direct patients' attention to ongoing hypnotic phenomena or events. This is done to enhance patients' awareness of hypnotic phenomena, or to direct their attention away from external events. One example would be 'Your limbs are starting to feel heavy and tired … so you can notice that you are starting to relax … '. The first part of the suggestion directs patients' attention to the experience of limb heaviness often characteristic of medium-depth hypnosis, whilst compounding the suggestion with the idea of relaxation. In this way patients will begin to associate the events of the hypnotic state with relaxation.

Individual aptitude

Positive attitude and expectation, patients' motivation for change and the rapport established between practitioner and patient are all factors in whether a practitioner can induce a hypnotic state. Influencing these factors is therefore a part of the pre-induction section of the clinical hypnosis session.

Evaluating the individual's potential to enter hypnosis or accept hypnotherapeutic suggestions is problematic and there are few accurate tests or indicators for susceptibility. The Stanford Hypnotic Susceptibility Scale (Weitzenhoffer and Hilgard, 1962) and the Harvard Group Scale of Hypnotic Susceptibility (Shor et al, 1962) are often referred to in clinical publications. These tests use standardised psychological tests that are performance-based to check for hypnotic susceptibility. It has been discovered that although susceptibility can be measured, it is not necessarily an accurate indicator of whether therapeutic suggestions will be accepted more readily. It is best to use evaluative processes that are based on patients' responses in the pre-induction section of the hypnosis session as a method of calibrating unique hypnotic susceptibility, and to base a treatment protocol around these responses rather than using hypnotic suggestibility or hypnotic susceptibility tests, which can damage the rapport between patient and practitioner.

Nor does the ability to experience the hypnotic state change much throughout patients' lifetimes, although studies of varying age groups appear to show that the responsiveness peaks between teenage years and the age of 35. The ability to be hypnotised appears to follow the normal bell-shaped curve for performance, with the younger and older age groups tending to demonstrate relatively lower responsiveness. Longitudinal studies in college students have shown that the ability to be hypnotised remains as stable as the IQ over a 25-year period (Piccone *et al.*, 1989).

Other factors which influence performance relate to patients' ability to experience hypnosis-related phenomena outside formal hypnosis. An example of this is found in studies by de Groot *et al.* (1988) and by Drake *et al.* (1990–1991), which show that patients with active imaginations are more likely to experience hypnotic phenomena, and therefore access deeper levels of hypnosis. Alongside this, Tellegen and Atkinson (1974) developed a scale of absorption to attempt to measure this phenomenon. The ability to become absorbed in a subject is an accurate indicator of how able a patient is to experience hypnosis.

Restricted environment stimulation therapy (REST) is the only process currently known to demonstrate the capability to enhance the individual's capacity to experience hypnotic states. As it implies, the patient is subjected to a restricted environment, such as a flotation. Studies by Barabasz and Barabasz (1989), on patients with chronic pain conditions, demonstrated an increased aptitude for hypnosis when the REST technique was used.

Normal states of consciousness

One of the common remarks made by those experiencing hypnosis is how similar it is to the waking state. Their expectations and belief structures, which are discussed elsewhere in this volume, are a factor in this. This is why it is important for the practitioner to explain the hypnotic state in terms of commonly occurring focused or altered states. Telling patients about daydreaming, or how it feels to be absorbed in a piece of music, is often a good way of leading them into an appreciation of how hypnosis can be experienced. It is always useful to describe the hypnotic event in terms of what will be familiar to patients as this ensures that they feel in control and enhances their receptivity to suggestions and can build on positive mental associations.

Physiological and perceptual indicators of stages of hypnotic state

There are no fixed delimiters to levels of hypnosis, nor do these levels have specific significance in terms of which will be most effective for the patient to receive suggestions. Each patient will settle on a level at which they feel comfortable and receptive at that time.

Light hypnosis

This is the first stage that any patient can enter, and, in a formal hypnosis induction, commences as soon as eye closure is achieved. With certain conditions and patients, this state is one that is a symptom of their condition, for example if the patient is dissociated. This can be observed particularly when patients are discussing their condition during the pre-induction talk, and physical indicators of dissociation are already present, for example a fixed gaze and slow responsiveness to questions.

The following events can be observed:

- eye closure
- movement is reduced
- swallow reflex becomes more pronounced
- posture and facial features begin to relax
- breathing begins to deepen
- external indicators of tension begin to decrease.

Medium hypnosis

Medium hypnosis is the next stage of hypnosis, in which the awareness of the patient moves from external to a more intensive concentration on internal events. Patients may notice their stomach rumbling, or become more aware of other internal processes such as their pulse.

The following events can be observed:

- head moves from upright position further backwards or forwards than usual
- slumped posture
- mouth may open

- skin pigmentation heightens
- feelings of lethargy
- feelings of tiredness
- characteristics of light hypnosis become more pronounced
- decreased awareness of immediate surroundings
- retardation in responsiveness
- reduction in sensory awareness
- twitching movements in the peripheral nervous system
- increased lachrymation
- breathing moves to abdomen
- yawning.

Deep hypnosis

This is the level at which suggestions are best received. Not all patients are able to access this level, and it is worthwhile noting at this point that when no further trance phenomena can be observed, and patients appear to 'plateau', they have reached a level of experience with which they are comfortable. Additional to this it is worth noting that response time to suggestions increases as greater depths of hypnosis are achieved, so more time may need to be given for patients to respond.

When patients reach their plateau, attempts to deepen further are usually ineffective, and it can be observed that they will start to shift around if the practitioner attempts to further deepen the trance.

The following events can be observed:

- characteristics of light and medium hypnosis further enhanced
- partial or total amnesia of the hypnotic events
- depersonalisation
- increased capacity to experience analgesia or anaesthesia
- enhanced capacity to experience hallucinatory states
- partial or total amnesia of suggestions made during hypnosis
- external awareness periodically closes down
- deep abdominal breathing
- sighing.

Somnambulism

When experienced during the hypnotic state, somnambulism allows patients to experience sensations and events as if they were awake. This is similar to the somnambulistic state that occurs during sleep. It is a rare occurrence, as the potential to experience somnambulism in hypnosis correlates to patients already having experienced these states in their sleep. As a therapeutic state it is not considered to be useful, as the amnesia that occurs as part of this state prevents patients from recalling suggestions once conscious. Even during the somnambulistic hypnotic state, the patient remains aware on some level and will not accept suggestions outside of their moral, social or emotional framework. In other words no-one, at any stage of experiencing hypnosis or post-hypnosis, can be 'made' to do something that they would not have otherwise been inclined to do.

The following events may be observed:

- eyes open
- tension in body and facial features
- may walk or talk
- experience amnesia in, and after, the hypnotic event
- failure to respond to suggestions.

Abreactions

An abreaction occurs during hypnosis when the patient gains access to emotional states that have not been experienced appropriately, or when there has been no opportunity for the patient to fully come to terms with an event. Abreactions are cathartic in nature, and allow patients to discharge their emotions in a safe environment. Whilst a patient is experiencing an abreaction the practitioner needs to ensure that the patient feels safe and is given permission to experience the emotion. An abreaction may take the form of tears or laughter, for example. It is essential that the practitioner does not make any assumptions about the nature of the abreaction whilst the patient is in hypnosis, for example to assume that tears necessarily denote sadness. Neutral language at this point is vital, and suggestions such as 'You are safe' and 'That's fine to let it out' can be made.

On waking patients after an abreaction it is appropriate to give them time to discuss it if they should wish, but they should not be questioned about the event. Often, patients experience feelings of tiredness after abreactions, and it is appropriate to compound suggestions in the post-hypnotic section of the session by suggesting that they will feel much better after a night's sleep.

An abreaction is not a necessity for patients to access emotional states, and care should be taken to ensure that no suggestions of this kind are made. If patients abreact spontaneously, that is, outside the framework of any suggestions being made at that time, it is important to reassure them that they abreacted because they felt safe to do so, and it will be of use for them. This is particularly important when patients express an opinion that they feel worse rather than better after the experience, so the abreaction is then reframed as part of their progress rather than otherwise. You may wish to use the model of a healing crisis to reframe the abreaction. This model utilises the image of a fever, which worsens before it improves, and suggestions are made that the abreaction is like the peak of the fever – things can now start to improve. Practitioners should not comment on the abreaction on waking the patient, as some individuals will have amnesia of the event.

The following events may be observed:

- laughter or tears
- shaking

- increased movement
- tension in facial features
- alterations in posture
- verbalisation of emotion
- alteration in skin pigmentation.

Managing patients during an abreaction

If a patient abreacts, the practitioner will need to acknowledge that they are aware of the event. This is done to reassure patients that they are being observed, and that the practitioner is not unduly concerned over the abreaction. This will give the patient a comfort zone to experience the event in any way that will be cathartic to them. The acknowledgement will be done by the practitioner using phrases such as 'That's fine … you are safe here … you can let it go … '. Care is taken to ensure that the phrases are neutral – in other words, that the practitioner is not assuming anything. Tears may signify joy, such as at the birth of a child, or laughter may be a way of discharging angry feelings. Neutral, reassuring phrases or even silence, will allow patients to go through the abreaction until they tire of it. If the patient appears to becoming very distressed by the abreaction, but still does not come out of hypnosis, the practitioner can ask for a signal such as a head nod, to signify that the patient would like to be brought out of hypnosis. Another way of getting patients away from the abreaction is to take them below the hypnotic level at which they are experiencing the event. Direct, authoritarian suggestions, such as 'Deep … deep sleep', can be made to take the patient away from the event and further into hypnosis. Deciding when to allow and when to intervene comes with experience. Abreactions often look worse than they actually are, and, as a general rule, it is better to allow the patient to experience it in a safe environment rather than having it continue to have some effect on them. It is safe to say that abreactions occur when patients feel safe with the practitioner, and they do have a cathartic effect, even if they can seem quite unpleasant for the patient at the time. They are *not* a necessary component in the efficacy of the hypnotherapeutic outcome, and it is for this reason that the practitioner does not explain the possibility of this happening before the induction, as this could induce anxiety and act as a self-fulfilling prophecy.

Falling asleep during hypnosis

It is important for the practitioner to continue to observe the patient throughout the process for many reasons, not least of which to ensure that the patient does not fall asleep during the process. This might occur if the patient is particularly tired, has been very stressed, or has not relaxed for a while. Older patients are also more inclined to drift off into sleep when relaxation suggestions are made.

It is preferable to prevent sleep from occurring. At the first indicator that the patient is moving from hypnosis into sleep, the practitioner can raise the voice or increase the speed of suggestions to hold the patient in the hypnotic state. If, however, the patient is already asleep, bringing a patient back from sleep to hypnosis can be done using one of two methods. The first is for the practitioner to gradually increase the rate at which they are breathing. This produces an atavistic response in the patient, during which the brain interprets the raised breathing pattern as heightened alertness – or potential anxiety in the practitioner – and therefore a situation has arisen to which they may need to pay more conscious attention. The patient's brain will then send out signals to wake and assess the situation. This is the response noticed during the Blitz in the Second World War, where mothers of young babies were able to sleep through the noise of bombing, but would wake if their child began stirring. Another way of gradually moving the patient from sleep to hypnosis it to increase the pace and volume of the suggestions, or vary the pattern of suggestions made. This too needs to be done gradually in order not to jerk the patient out of hypnosis. If the practitioner is observing and calibrating the patient's changing responses, the patient should be able to move from sleep to deep relaxation without coming all the way out of hypnosis.

As already mentioned, this change in state from hypnosis to sleep can be observed by changes in breathing patterns and increased movement. If sleep does occur, the practitioner has a choice. If therapeutic suggestions have been made *before* the patient fell asleep, the practitioner may wish to allow the patient to sleep and wake normally when they have taken sufficient benefit from the relaxation. If therapeutic suggestions have yet to be made when the patient falls asleep, it is more appropriate to bring them out of sleep and aim to keep them in hypnosis.

Contraindications for the use of clinical hypnosis

Not everyone is able to experience hypnosis, or is receptive to the therapeutic suggestions. There are certain individuals, and specific conditions, which have as part of their modus operandi, the equivalent of a switch which prevents them from being receptive to the type of altered state experienced during hypnosis, and, by default, the therapeutic suggestions.

Conditions

Any condition for which the patient is currently undergoing medical intervention requires the clinical hypnosis practitioner to gain permission from a medical practitioner. There are no absolutes with regard to what can and cannot be treated. The capacity to treat depends on the setting, for example in a hospital, and under the supervision of a medical practitioner, and also the other competencies and skills of the person doing the hypnosis, for example a midwife using hypnosis for childbirth.

Medications

If the patient is taking medications designed to alter the chemistry of the brain, these can alter the patient's susceptibility to suggestions. If this is the situation, it becomes a factor in whether to use hypnosis. Certain medications for depression, for example, fall under this heading. In addition to this there may be side-effects of medications which are similar to hypnotic phenomena, and could therefore make the experience of hypnosis a less than positive one for the patient.

Symptoms

Some conditions have symptoms that the patient may experience as phenomena when in the hypnotic state. An example of this would be the sensations of drifting or floating which are sometimes experienced during hypnosis, and might be associated with the symptomatic dissociation of depression, or sensory hallucinations, which might be disturbing for someone with migraine, and be sufficient to bring on an attack. It is essential therefore for the practitioner to take full note of the ways in which patients experience their symptoms when deciding on the appropriacy of their use.

Individuals

The normal states of awareness (7±2)

It is worthwhile at this point to be aware that although most individuals can be hypnotised, there is a framework that can be used to evaluate whether it is appropriate, and what type of suggestions would be applicable to this type of individual.

The '7±2 model' refers to the number of pieces of information that are stored in the short-term memory at any one moment in time. Seven is considered to be normal functioning. When eight pieces of information are present, the individual is operating above normal levels, and the term for this is 'neurotic'. Neurotic functioning is still healthy, provided that when the requirement to process the extra piece of information is no longer present, that is, when the individual no longer has the heightened workload, or problem to deal with, they return to a normal level of functioning (seven). Add a further item to the list, and the individual has nine items of information in the short-term memory. This processing is labelled 'psychotic', and is outside the range of healthy functioning. The psychosis may involve voices giving instructions (suggestions) and the individual will certainly be on medication. Therefore individuals at this level of processing are not suitable candidates for hypnosis as they are unable to rest sufficiently to enter hypnosis.

At the other end of the scale there are those who have six items in the short-term memory, and are operating at the slower end of the scale. The term used for this scenario is 'lethargic', and, like neurotic, it is still considered healthy functioning provided the individual can shift gear into normal functioning when necessary. The final category is that of 'catatonic', with five pieces of information in the short-term memory at any one moment in time. As with psychotic processing, these individuals are outside the range of the use of hypnosis. They will be on medication, and will find the focus required to enter hypnosis very difficult, if not impossible.

In summary: the normal (seven items), neurotic (eight items) and lethargic (six items) all fall within the range of functioning whereby clinical hypnosis may be used. For neurotic individuals, suggestions can be made to reduce stress or let go of their neurosis; for lethargic individuals, suggestions for motivation and focus can be made. Individuals who are processing information normally may wish to break a habit or alter an unwanted thought or behaviour. From this we can see that the way in which individuals function will have a bearing on how they manage their condition, and therefore on selecting the most appropriate strategy with which to treat.

Common-sense considerations

There are also common-sense indications as to when it is not appropriate to use hypnosis. Examples would be when the patient is unwilling to experience it, or when the suggestions are not for the direct benefit of the patient. If the patient is under the influence of alcohol or recreational drugs, or in any form of artificially induced altered state it is not advisable to attempt to induce hypnosis. Additionally, the use of hypnosis for entertainment is also not appropriate for those who practise it in the medical setting, so if someone wants to experience it purely as an experiment it is unlikely to work.

As a further note, if individuals do ask for hypnosis but they do not have any specific reason for wishing to experience it, this can fall under one of three headings. One is the prospective patient who does not wish to disclose the nature of their condition; another is one who is simply curious about the experience. The final category is individuals for whom the process would not be appropriate because of an undiagnosed pre-existing condition or if they have an inappropriate objective for the hypnosis session. An example of this is the individual who believes that something has happened to them and if they can only uncover what it might be, then 'everything will be all right'.

It is important for the practitioner to use safeguards to ensure where possible that they can assist genuine cases, and deselect those for whom the process could be harmful or dangerous. If the practitioner suspects it to be the case that the patient is being less than truthful about the nature of their requirement to be hypnotised, the recommended course of action is for the non-medical practitioner of hypnosis to request that the prospective subject of hypnosis visits their own medical practitioner and has a medical evaluation. The prospective patient must then request written permission allowing the clinical hypnosis practitioner to treat, and this is to be obtained before any hypnotherapeutic session can be booked. The net result of this is that the clinical hypnosis practitioner will then be safe in the knowledge that the patient has been properly evaluated for the symptoms of their condition, and those for whom hypnosis would not be appropriate have been identified. This means also that the safety of the practitioner and the prospective patient is, where possible, ensured. It is generally recognised that individuals who have reasons other than those initially given to the clinical hypnosis practitioner will rarely visit their doctor and so deselect themselves from the process. There is always the possibility that there are individuals who could be helped who will slip through the net at this point, but the lay practitioner of hypnosis does not have the medical knowledge to diagnose a condition, and referral to a medical practitioner is the appropriate ethical course of action to take in these circumstances.

To summarise, before making a decision to use clinical hypnosis, the individual, the condition and the patient's interaction with the condition (symptoms and effects) will need to be taken into account and evaluated. Here lies one of the reasons why clinical hypnosis research currently fails to meet the research criteria required for its use within mainstream medicine. At present there are numerous protocols for using clinical hypnosis with medical conditions. The failure in research seems to lie in the inability to agree standardised procedures that relate to the pre-evaluation process. What has happened in research up to this point is mainly a large number of small-scale research projects, each employing different methodologies, which cannot be compared with each other, and which fail to reflect the wider potential of clinical hypnosis. A common conclusion drawn in many clinical hypnosis trials is that more clinical trials are required to assess appropriately the use of clinical hypnosis as a mainstream medical intervention. The key here is to recognise that the pre-evaluation process, and the way in which decisions are made on the form and content of hypnotherapeutic suggestions, is an essential component of the protocol. This process can be identified and standardised. Some clinical hypnosis practitioners would argue that by doing so, the freedom to utilise instinct when selecting suggestions or building rapport is taken away, and that this would adversely affect the potential results. To a degree they are correct. However, for clinical hypnosis to achieve the status of a recognised medical tool, efficacy might need to be compromised to create standardised procedures that can then be modified according to the preferences of the individual.

References

Barabasz AF and Barabasz M (1989) Effects of restricted environment stimulation: enhancement of hypnotisability for experimental and chronic pain control. *Int J Clin Exp Hypn* **39(3): 217–31.**

Drake S, Nash M and Cawood G (1990–1991) Imaginative involvement and hypnotic susceptibility: a re-examination of the relationship. *Imag, Cogn Per.* **10:** 141–55.

de Groot H, Gwynn M and Spanos N (1988) The effects of contextual information and gender on the prediction of hypnotic susceptibility. *J Pers Soc Psychol.* **54**: 1049–53.

Piccione C, Hilgard ER and Zimbardo PG (1989) On the degree of stability of measured hypnotizability over a 25-year period. *J Pers Soc Psychol.* **56**: 289–95.

Shor R and Orne E (1962) *The Harvard Group Scale of Hypnotic Susceptibility . Forms A & B.* Consulting Psychologists Press, Palo Alto.

Tellegen A and Atkinson G (1974) Openness to absorbing and self-altering experiences ('absorption'), a trait related to hypnotic susceptibility. *J Ab Psychol.* **83**: 268–77.

Weitzenhoffer AM and Hilgard ER (1962) *Stanford Hypnotic Susceptibility Scale.* Consulting Psychologists Press, Palo Alto.

Chapter 6

Therapeutic approaches within hypnosis

Before any decisions can be made as to the type of approach to be used, the components that will make an individual more receptive to one approach rather than another need to be identified and evaluated against the following criteria:

* motivation to experience hypnosis
* stress as a component of their condition
* the mindset of the individual
* the patient has a specific therapeutic objective.

The motivation to experience hypnosis has already been discussed elsewhere in this volume. How to use this information to select the appropriate approach for an individual patient, and set therapeutic objectives is covered in Chapter 7, 'Creating the hypnotherapeutic protocol'.

Stress as a component of patients' conditions

Stress will cause patients to further focus attention on themselves in a neurotic or unhealthy manner, which then exacerbates the symptom. The other consideration here is that when individuals are given better coping mechanisms for stress their confidence increases, their ability to function more appropriately increases, and their sense of perspective over their problem will necessarily increase. All these factors will have an effect on the symptoms and affects of the condition.

The mindset of the individual

As to the mindset of the individual, provided an environment is created for patients to feel able to relax, their mindset can be adapted to one which will be effective in helping them make changes. The practitioner must therefore evaluate each condition in relation to the mindset which patients bring to their approach to treatment. Patients' expectations of hypnosis will have a bearing on the efficacy of treatment. Interestingly, patients who expect hypnosis to 'cure' them, or who want very badly to experience hypnosis will rarely gain maximum benefit from this intervention. As already mentioned, an extreme desire to experience hypnosis will increase anxiety levels, and produce the effect of a failure to enter the relaxed hypnotic state. It may be that patients' expectations are so high that personal motivation to change remains low. Whichever is the case, it is those patients who present with a sceptical, though open mind, who tend to experience most benefit.

Once all other factors are taken into consideration and a specific objective can be identified with the patient, the type of protocol to be used can be decided upon.

The following are a number of different hypnotherapeutic approaches. These have been selected on the basis that the pre-selection criteria already discussed in this book can be applied in mapping the internal structure of a clinical hypnosis session, and then personalising it to the patient. The practitioner is then able to qualify and quantify the decisions made in relation to the approach selected. There are other hypnotherapeutic approaches which are potentially no less effective, but as the decision-making criteria are not so transparent, they have been excluded here.

The approaches discussed here vary widely from the strictly clinical to the borderline esoteric. It is essential to remember when selecting the approach that it is the opinions of the patient that are paramount in selecting the approach. If the practitioner does not favour that approach because of their own personal beliefs, these beliefs are best put aside while working with that particular patient, unless the practitioner believes that the approach favoured by the patient could be potentially harmful. In the clinical hypnosis framework practitioners operate as a tabula rasa, and should not impose their belief structures on patients.

When first practising clinical hypnosis there are occasions when practitioners do not choose the most obvious or appropriate approach for their patients because they themselves do not like it, or are not confident with the technique. As practitioners grow in knowledge and experience, the approaches they will use should increase in number – otherwise their range will become increasingly narrow and they will only be effective with a small number of patients with an ever-decreasing success rate. Having a wide range of approaches from which to select the most appropriate will allow the clinical hypnosis practitioner to help a greater number of individuals with a wider range of conditions. Furthermore, the result of doing the same approach and using it with a small group of individuals can eventually reduce motivation, and even rapport and observation skills. The best clinical hypnosis practitioners will have one field of personal expertise, but will continue to practise different approaches and with other conditions as a way of continuing to refine their skills.

It is an interesting fact that a specialist in one condition or approach rarely sets out to work in that area. It will often be the case that they have a success with a particular condition – and that others with that condition will come to see them as a result of their success, and that they will refine their skills by working with large numbers of individuals with that condition. By then, the practitioner's skills are attuned to the nuances of how these patients interact with their condition and so their expertise will be enhanced. In effective clinical hypnosis tuition the student is encouraged to attempt approaches which are outside their personal experience or comfort zone. In this way individuals becomes less judgemental and more open when selecting approaches for the benefit of their patients, rather than for their own personal reasons. It is also a recognised fact that when practitioners use an approach which they would not have selected, and they observe this technique working with a patient, they will encompass it into their range of experience, become comfortable and proficient with it, and their personal outlook will therefore broaden and benefit both themselves and their patients. That is not to say that an individual will become comfortable with using all approaches, just that it is important to continue to learn techniques, and to further develop the range of skills when practising clinical hypnosis on a regular basis.

Specific hypnotherapeutic approaches

What follows is an introduction to the many ways in which therapeutic processes can be conducted within the framework of hypnosis. Regardless of the form of clinical hypnosis protocol selected by the practitioner, the primary aim is the alleviation of a symptom or a problem. In no circumstances should an untutored practitioner use these techniques for experimentation. When dealing with the mind of another patient, or even oneself, it is possible to inadvertently trigger emotions or apparent memories, which would then need to be processed in an appropriate manner. Only in an educational setting or some other controlled environment with supervision is it appropriate to experience these techniques without a clearly defined outcome in mind.

As has already been discussed, the practitioner does not need to have a specific belief structure to utilise any of the following methods. An open attitude is all that is required. Under the protocol heading are suggested conditions or types of individuals that would respond well to each. The lists are by no means exhaustive.

Ericksonian

This technique is based on the work of Milton H Erickson, who is regarded as the father of modern-day hypnosis. In its purest form, Ericksonian hypnosis involves open-eye hypnosis, where there is no formal induction of a hypnotic state. The practitioner will give indirect or open-ended suggestions based on the personality and environment of the patient, and focuses the patient on the possibilities of change. This technique aims to elicit the solution to their condition from the unconscious of the patient, often using 'confusion as the gateway to learning'. This approach places emphasis on suggesting through open-ended questions and the use of analogies. This encourages different ways for the patient to think about their condition and draw alternative conclusions on the ways to act and respond. Ericksonian hypnosis gives the linguistic structure on which many other hypnotherapeutic approaches are based.

Applications

- analytical individuals
- confidence building
- anxiety
- habitual behaviours.

Traditional

This form of hypnosis includes a formal induction, involving eye closure, and a deepener usually based around physical suggestions such as progressive muscle relaxation. The therapeutic suggestions are usually delivered in the form of direct suggestions based on the specific objective for therapy which is uncovered in the pre-induction talk. This type of approach can be more authoritarian in the nature of suggestions, and is best used with patients who have a healthy ego state and a clear idea of their objectives. To refer back to the section on 'Individuals' in Chapter 6, these would be the people with seven pieces of information in their short-term memory – those people who are otherwise 'normal' but might wish to break a habit, or refine a behaviour.

Applications

- habit breaking
- motivation
- performance enhancement.

Esoteric

Esoteric techniques include any form of hypnosis that incorporates the patient's belief structure but may not, initially, appear to be directly related to the problem. An example of this would be rebirthing or past-life regression therapy. With an esoteric approach, the patient would usually have expressed the belief that this particular approach will work for them, and will be able to explain the ways in which they believe it will benefit them. In the clinical setting, esoteric approaches are not necessarily to be considered as the first choice – except in the situation where patients have built the expectation of this approach being the most effective for them into their mindset about hypnosis. Before choosing an esoteric approach the practitioner will need to identify clear objectives for the patient, as some esoteric techniques do not lend themselves easily to creating specific and realistic outcomes for therapy.

Applications

- relationships
- grief
- indecision
- individuals with a personal belief structure in the process.

Rebirthing

This process is one of reliving one's own birth process. The objective of rebirthing is re-experiencing any associated feelings, and to revivify a component of the birth event in order to release individuals from any perceived traumas which occurred during their birth. The theory of this technique states that once this has occurred and been processed fully by the individual, a remission from the associated symptom can be obtained. An example of this could be a patient who has claustrophobia, and experiencing the rebirthing process 'uncovers' a traumatic birth experience during which they recall having the umbilical cord around their neck at the time of delivery. Once the experience is processed consciously the requirement for the symptom is then eliminated. Rebirthing is also used outside the framework of clinical hypnosis and can involve a physical process which is used to simulate the experience of birth.

Applications

- individuals with a personal belief structure in the process
- analytical individuals.

Direct suggestions

A direct suggestion is where the content is explicit. Direct suggestions are goal-driven and are therefore based on what patients require in terms of change (for example, more energy), rather than what they do not require (for example, not tired). Direct suggestions are effective in habit breaking, in confirming events, and are effective in ego-strengthening to direct patients' attention towards external events which already exist, but to which they have not previously paid attention. When in hypnosis, patients appreciate the certainty of direct suggestions, as the practitioner will use them to confirm positive states and to affirm new behaviours and thought processes. Direct suggestions are more authoritarian than permissive, as they involve instructing the patient in what to do. If patients are anxious or depressed, or their mindset is one which does not lend itself to being told what they should do or what to experience, direct suggestion should be used sparingly, if at all.

Applications

- habit breaking
- performance enhancement
- phobias
- stress management.

Indirect suggestions

This type of suggestion uses terms such as 'may', 'can' and 'if you wish' to direct patients' attention in a specific way without engaging conscious objections. In clinical hypnosis this approach incorporates a factor known as 'apparent choice'. Apparent choice is when two or more alternatives are presented to patients and they are asked to make a choice of either/or. The practitioner will either direct the patient's preference to one of the choices, or regardless of which the patient chooses the objective is achieved. Therefore, implicit in any indirect suggestion is the objective, for example, 'You may find your eyelids becoming heavy and tired ... wanting to close ... they may wish to close now ... or they may wish to close later'. Either way, the objective of eye closure will be achieved. Indirect suggestions can allow the practitioner to express one suggestion in a number of ways, and to repeat suggestions until they are accepted by the patient. This type of suggestion is also known as 'permissive suggestion'.

Applications

- chronic pain
- anxiety
- children
- first time experience of hypnosis.

Neurolinguistic programming-based techniques

Neurolinguistic programming (NLP) is a framework created by Richard Bandler and John Grinder, and is based on the works of Milton Erickson. NLP is a methodology of communication that identifies the modalities in which individuals communicate. It utilises structured language patterns, and places value on the levels at which we communicate, either at a deep (meaning) level or a surface (social) level. It is used to evaluate behaviour and thought processes, and to create specific structures to change and improve them. Clinical hypnosis can use NLP techniques within the hypnotic state, and incorporate these communication patterns into the therapeutic suggestions. This allows patients to receive suggestions in a structured manner, and incorporate them into their thoughts and behaviours in a way that will be acceptable to them. NLP is, however, most obviously employed in clinical hypnosis in the pre-induction talk and within the context of the specific therapeutic suggestions.

Applications

- low self-esteem
- confidence building
- phobic responses
- performance enhancement.

Hypno-desensitisation

This is a hypnotherapeutic protocol that utilises the well-documented psychological approach of desensitisation. The patient is required to produce a scale of disturbance (known as a SUDS scale) itemising the least to the highest anxiety-evoking situation within the framework of their condition. Once the scale is produced, hypnosis is then induced and a signalling device is installed. The practitioner will then describe the events, commencing with the least anxiety-evoking, and make suggestions of relaxation at each point. Where no or minimal anxiety is experienced, the next event on the hierarchy is presented. Where anxiety is experienced, additional relaxation is suggested, until minimal or no anxiety is experienced. This process is continued throughout the hierarchy.

Applications

- phobias
- pain control
- performance anxiety
- stress management.

Quantum therapy

In the context of clinical hypnosis, quantum therapy uses two basic strategies. With the first, the practitioner seeks to assist the patient in moving outside of their habitual thought processes or behaviours. The second relates to the concept that the patient maintains the problem by continuing to pay attention to symptoms on an unconscious and conscious level. Guided imagery is used to lead the patient into a state of momentary 'chaos', from which a new version of reality will be created. At that point, appropriate thoughts and behaviours will then become accessible.

Applications

- behavioural changes
- indecision
- dermatology
- neurotic conditions.

Polarity

Polarity-based techniques use the basic premiss that if you have experience of one type of state or event, you have the latent knowledge of the opposite state and can potentially experience it to the same degree. In this framework, the mindset which created the condition contains recognition of an equal and opposite mindset. The end result will be a balanced state by recognising both ends of the scale at the same time.

Applications

- creativity
- decision-making
- repetitive negative thought patterns
- over-stimulated nervous system (for example, hormones).

Creative visualisations

Creative visualisations can be incorporated into a number of other approaches. The basic premiss here is the use of suggested images to create a representational system. Once an image has been created to represent the patient's condition, or the patient's interaction with their condition (symptoms or affects) or even of their objective, then this image can be altered. Once patients take control of the images this allows them to then make those changes in reality. An example of the types of changes which can be made would be assisting in recovery from cardiovascular problems, where the scarring on the heart is visualised and the image is changed to a strong, healthy heart as recovery takes place. Other creative visualisations are more analytical in intent, where individuals produce a safe environment wherein they can come to terms with an aspect of their problem. Metaphors, quantum and mind – body techniques fall into this category.

Applications

- recovery from surgery
- grief
- coping with cancer and side-effects of medical intervention
- abuse.

Psychoneuroimmunology

Psychoneuroimmunology (PNI) is a mind–body technique using imagery primarily to stimulate the immune system. PNI is used as an adjunct to conventional applications and is best known for its use in oncology. PNI works with stress, the psyche and the immune system to create distractions, enhance patients' perception of control over their condition, and enhance the efficacy of medication and other treatment strategies.

Applications

- oncology
- pain control
- immune disorders
- healing after physical injuries.

Time distortion

Time distortion techniques in clinical hypnosis are used to expand time for those who need more time, and contract time for those for whom time drags. As time distortion is a symptom of some common conditions, particularly those that involve anxiety – this approach allows patients to alter their perception of time to increase or decrease the time experience. The phenomena of time distortion in the hypnotic state can be used to help convince the patient that some-thing different from the normal state of awareness has occurred whilst they were hypnotised.

Applications

- premature ejaculation
- memory and learning
- childbirth
- recovery and healing.

Dissociative techniques

Dissociative techniques operate on the premiss that a condition has a component in which the patient feels they are not in control when experiencing a symptom. This is often described by the patient as 'a part of me which seems to take over when … (insert symptom), for example bingeing'. Dissociative techniques follow a sequence whereby the part in control of the symptom is:

- identified
- the needs of the part are identified
- these needs are negotiated
- the part is reintegrated into the whole individual and the symptom is returned under the direct control of the patient.

The patient may then require a further technique to gain full remission from the symptom; this usually takes the form of deconditioning (hypno-desensitisation or direct suggestions to eliminate the habitual component of the symptom).

Applications

- nail biting
- binge eating
- obsessive compulsive disorders (such as trichotillomania)
- trauma.

Regression

Regression, when utilised in hypnosis, allows patients to experience a past event, real or imagined, through which they can analyse and gain insight into their cur-rent situation or condition. When using clinical hypnosis, the patient having the experience of the past event whilst in hypnosis and in a safe and controlled envi-ronment, is purely to assist them to move forward. A more rare use of regression is to allow the patient to experience an event in order to recall a specific element of that event, for example if an object has been lost and the patient cannot recall where they put it.

Applications

- hay fever
- memory recall
- blushing
- reconnecting with older, more appropriate behaviour patterns.

Esoteric regression

Also known as 'past life' regression is a process in which patients access a 'past life experience' that they perceive to be in some way relevant to their current situation or condition. During the past life patients undergo various stages of progression whereby they can gain insight into feelings and events, thereby experiencing catharsis.

Applications

- relationships
- maladaptive behavioural patterns
- analysis of current behaviours or responses.

Non-verbal communication

Non-verbal suggestion is a method of supplementing other techniques in, or out of, the hypnotic state. By being congruent in tone, pitch and volume with the verbal suggestions they can be amplified, or by being incongruent they can encourage patients to question the veracity of the statement. Physical movements or utilisation of pauses between statements also comes under this technique.

Applications

- hypnosis for the deaf or hearing-impaired
- hypnosis with children
- kinaesthetic patients.

Automatic writing and drawing

This approach uses the ideo-motor movements of the hand as a medium for communicating information directly from unconscious to conscious awareness without it having to travel via the language centre. It is most useful for uncovering information that has not been spoken of, or an experience that took place during a trauma, such as a traffic accident. An example in this instance would be recollection of a vehicle licence plate that had previously been 'forgotten'. Automatic writing and drawing can also be used with regression, and patients will write as they would have written at the age to which they have been regressed. Only the patient can interpret the writing or drawing.

Applications

- discovering lost objects
- gaining insight into events
- trauma.

Ideo-motor response techniques

These techniques use fine motor movements, primarily finger movements to allow a patient to communicate otherwise suppressed information. Ideo-motor response (IMR) therapies draw upon the concept that patients have the answer to their condition within their unconscious. IMR allows the practitioner to operate as a facilitator in the negotiation between the patients' unconscious desires, and conscious processing. This negotiation can be carried out in a content-free manner allowing patients to release a neurotic symptom without consideration as to how this process is going to occur.

Applications

- behaviour modification
- blushing
- anxiety
- decision-making.

Hypno-drama

Similar in concept to psycho-drama (Julius Moreno), both involve the creation of a framework whereby patients can explore their responses, and those of other participants in an event, in a number of different situations. This in turn helps patients to 'play out' or direct the scene in various ways. The insight resulting from experiencing the viewpoint of others, observing their own behaviour in different ways and manipulating scenes then influences patients' attitudes over their own behaviour and that of others. The advantages of hypno-drama over psycho-drama are twofold. In psycho-drama the individuals involved in the events will be physically present, or represented externally. In hypnosis the patient can experience a much wider range of situations and emotions safely, and will be able to stop and start the scenes at will to explore variations on a theme. In both hypno- and psycho-drama the patient may also play different roles. The objective is to gain insight and perspective. The other advantage of hypno-drama is that it involves a relaxed state, and the patient will therefore be able to process the information more rapidly. Lastly, as the hypnosis is a multi-sensory experience, it is a potentially more enriching experience as direct suggestions can be made by the practitioner while the patient is in hypnosis – on more appropriate ways of feeling, thinking and acting in the scenario which they have just experienced.

Applications

- assertive training
- anger management
- abuse – drug or alcohol
- abuse – physical or emotional.

Inner game

This therapeutic application, based on a coaching technique, uses the premiss of an inner game and outer game being played out when an individual attempts to make change. The outer game involves logic and practicality and is concerned with influencing external events, whereas the inner game involves emotions, preconceptions and beliefs about the self. When applied in the context of clinical hypnosis, the inner game uses these structures to create an inner event that is congruent with the outer requirements – so the individual can fulfil peak performance. As with hypno-drama, the use of the hypnotic state enhances the images required to produce this required state of positive self-belief, and will amplify the benefits by the use of future projection (whereby the patient pre-experiences achieving the required changes) and sensory imagery so that patients can feel what it is like to achieve their goals.

Applications

- motivation
- self-sabotage
- goal-setting
- sensory modification.

Lucid dreaming

A technique that also exists outside of the framework of hypnosis: when used in hypnosis it is as an analytical method that aims to direct patients to use their dream state for processing information which will then help them gain a remission from their symptom. Suggestions are made during hypnosis that patients can first become aware of when they are dreaming (hence lucid) and they then experience the required outcome to their problem during the dream. It is most effective for patients who have a Jungian framework, or who have previously found that after sleeping well they can find the answer to some of their problems, or individuals who have an analytical approach to their condition. Some of the more esoterically minded individuals will also appreciate this technique.

Applications

- nocturnal enuresis
- nightmares
- enhance creative states
- sleep disorders.

Glove anaesthesia or analgesia

This technique is taught to patients as a method of pain control. It is a kinaesthetic technique in which suggestions of numbness or coolness are made to produce a dissociative event in the hand, coupled with hallucinations of the suggested change in sensations. It is known as 'glove anaesthesia' because the hallucination of changed sensations in the hand is created with suggestions that the patient is wearing a thick leather glove. It is used to bring about alleviation of physical pain by manipulating the sensations at the site of the pain.

The ability to create anaesthesia in the hand is taught to the patient and the patient is then taught self-hypnosis to increase the profundity of the anaesthesia or analgesia. The patient is then shown how to relocate the numbness or coolness from the hand to the site of pain. The relaxation induced by the self-hypnosis and the ability to manipulate the pain sensations generally improves the wellbeing of the patient, even if full anaesthesia is not achieved. This technique is frequently taught to reduce pain in labour, and is effective in dermatological conditions.

Applications

- pain management
- phantom limb
- healing
- childbirth.

Metaphor

A metaphorical suggestion uses a simple story that contains a covert, or secondary, meaning. The intention is to keep the conscious processes occupied with the story while the covert meaning is taken on board without engaging the critical processes. It is most effective with analytical patients as it allows them to analyse part of the process (the story), whilst accepting the inherent meaning.

Applications

- hypnosis with children
- pain management
- healing trauma
- fertility and pregnancy.

Hypno-analysis

This process involves identifying and analysing the origin or the construction of a problem. This method operates on the basic assumption that once this information has come into the consciousness, the impact of the problem can be reduced or removed. This process often involves regression to the time of origin, and is used for patients who have a perceived requirement to understand their behaviour or condition before expressing a willingness to move forward.

Application

• comprehension of thoughts, behaviours and emotions.

Cognitive – behavioural

This technique is based around changing negative self-beliefs. Once these belief patterns are identified and amended the associated behaviours can then be eliminated. When used in the framework of clinical hypnosis, this technique can enhance the patient's capacity to make the necessary mental connections, with less conscious objection, and therefore for change, more rapidly.

Applications

• maladaptive or repetitive thought processes
• working with limiting belief structures
• pattern breaking
• abuse of drugs or alcohol.

Chapter 7

Creating the hypnotherapeutic protocol

The use of questions to create the hypnotherapeutic protocol

This is a large topic and this chapter can only give an overview on how to create the therapeutic protocol. The skills of observation, active listening and interpretation come with experience, but they can also be learnt. These skills will become part of the decision-making process as practitioners gather examples of ways in which the protocols can be best put together from their own practice. In this chapter are examples of the types of questions necessary to devise an appropriate protocol, and the chapter also contains a simplistic model of how to put this information together.

There are two types of questions that are relevant in creating the hypnotherapeutic protocol: questions designed to uncover factual information and those designed for evaluative purposes. How these questions are delivered is not important, provided that they are put in such a way that patients feel comfortable enough to disclose the relevant information. Later in this chapter the structure follows the headings from Chapter 3, 'The structure of the clinical hypnosis session', and gives examples of the types of questions which can be used to elicit the information required for each component of the session. A session cannot be completely scripted as the practitioner will respond to the patient when eliciting information. The questions are to be used as prompts where the patient does not otherwise offer the relevant information when relaxed and a good rapport has been established. Once patients feel comfortable to talk about themselves they will often furnish the relevant information unprompted.

The questions are asked in the pre-induction discussion, except where otherwise described.

Areas to be covered in the questions are:

- the condition
- the most appropriate protocol
- the optimum time-frame for a remission from the symptoms or affects
- the patient's language patterns
- the patient's success states
- specific symptoms or affects
- duration and history of condition
- expectations of hypnosis and hypnotherapy
- selecting modality for delivery of therapeutic suggestions.

To recapitulate, there are six stages to a clinical hypnosis session: introduction, induction, deepening, post-hypnotic (therapeutic suggestions), the awakening stage and the final stage – post-hypnosis. The final stage consists of debriefing the patient. The questions are asked mainly in the pre-induction talk, except where otherwise shown. Questions will be shown in this chapter under the most relevant header, so it can be clearly seen to what the questioning refers.

To create the hypnotherapeutic therapeutic protocol there are four areas to be addressed, evaluated and taken into consideration. The purpose of this is to personalise the treatment, and to ensure where possible that the patient takes control of the process as part of the therapeutic partnership described elsewhere. A failing in some hypnotherapeutic processes is that the focus for the patient remains on the condition and the practitioner then attempts to treat the problem only. An example would be the assumption that, for a patient with a phobia of flying, the patient wished to be able to fly in an aeroplane – when their specific objective may be to be able to look at one in the sky without experiencing anxiety. It is for this reason that clear and specific objectives are required from the patient before the hypnotherapeutic process can commence.

The four areas for consideration and evaluation are:

- the patient
- the condition
- the interaction between patient and condition (the symptoms and effects)
- the objective.

First, the practitioner will need to isolate each of these components and evaluate them individually, and then take an overview of their interaction with one another. This takes place in the first contact (which may be a telephone call or email enquiry) and in the pre-induction talk. It will also continue as part of the post-hypnosis feedback session.

First-contact assessment

The first contact may be a telephone call, email or the first session itself. The purpose of first contact is to reject any prospective candidates for hypnotherapy who may not be suitable because of individual characteristics, or if the condition with which they are presenting is contraindicated for the use of hypnosis. This process may seem an obvious one, and is for the protection of patients and practitioners, and any patient who is not deemed suitable for hypnotherapy can be assured of this. Once this process has occurred (*see* Chapter 5, the section on contraindications for the use of clinical hypnosis (p. 54) for the evaluation criteria), the next objective is to identify the patient's objective in general terms.

The following are key phrases that can be used to elicit this initial information. Such phrases can be used as guidelines on how most appropriately to construct questions:

'How can I help you?'

This phrase is used as a way of identifying the presenting condition, and will give the practitioner an indication as to the patient's preconceptions and level of motivation, all of which takes place without the patient needing to focus on the problem. This negative focus of attention would be the case if the practitioner asked 'What is the problem?'.

Implicit in the 'How can I help you?' question is the statement, 'How do *you think* hypnotherapy can help you?', which will encourage patients to focus on the role of hypnotherapy in creating the change they require.

The patient's response to the question when phrased in this way will be to present their condition, and often to identify their conception of the role of hypnosis in helping them. An example would be, 'I want to stop smoking, and a friend of mine told me hypnosis is a good way of doing this.' From this the practitioner can start to evaluate the mindset of the patient. Conversely, if the patient says, 'I don't *really* want to stop smoking, my doctor told me to come here', the practitioner is also gaining information that the patient's motivation will be an aspect they need to incorporate into the script if they chose to go ahead with the session.

With most conditions, it is appropriate to ask whether the patient is seeing a medical practitioner or taking medication for their condition. If this is the case it is appropriate for the practitioner to say:

'You will need to visit your GP and let them know that you are intending to have hypnotherapy. I will need their consent in writing.'

This has the effect of putting the prescribing physician in the information loop, so when writing up the case the clinical hypnosis practitioner can send them a copy for the patient's medical records. Additionally, if the patient has not seen their medical practitioner, they can do so and have the condition diagnosed appropriately. There will be some people who, when asked to do this, will choose not to do so, and therefore do not come back to make the appointment. There may be any number of reasons for this. Some people, for example, will decide that they have a phobia based on nothing more than a magazine article. It is important to be aware that this process of ensuring that the medical practitioner has seen the patient first is put in place as a safeguard for non-medical practitioners to ensure that they are working with properly diagnosed conditions.

If the presenting condition falls within the categories of habit-breaking, or any other condition that could occur to anyone within the 'normal' range of experience, it is still appropriate to ask:

'Are you seeing a medical practitioner for any other condition?' or 'Are you currently taking any medication?'

By the use of this question, any other considerations which might be contraindicated can be identified. If the patient is taking medication which has side-effects similar to the phenomena of hypnosis, or which are mood mediators, it can compromise the efficacy or even the appropriacy of using hypnosis.

Introduction

This is the pre-induction talk in which most of the information-gathering and evaluation will be covered.

Information-gathering

Pinpoint the condition and review the information gathered from the first contact. This is kept to a minimum:

> 'You have told me on the phone that you would like to [pinpoint condition, for example, stop smoking].'

Then the framework of the session is introduced to the patient. This will allow the patient to know what to expect of the session, and begin to reduce their anxiety levels induced by fear of the unknown:

> 'What will happen in the hypnosis is you will have your eyes closed and I will make some suggestions to relax your body (or focus your attention). Then you will hear me make suggestions based on what we will discuss in this part of the session. I will only suggest what we have discussed; in fact, if I make any suggestions which you have not already agreed, you will, of course, wake yourself up and reject them. When this part of the hypnosis is over, I will wake you up, and you will become alert, feeling refreshed and relaxed. You will remember everything that is important for you to remember.'

Information about the patient as an individual is then requested. This is done to relax the patient, to develop rapport and to begin to learn about how they process information and to gain insight into the individual's personality and how resource states can be elicited. By starting with general, non-threatening questions, the patient will feel more comfortable and begin to speak freely. The information obtained in this section mainly relates to individuals and how they operate outside the framework of their condition:

> 'Tell me a little about yourself, what do you do for a living / where do you live / are you in a relationship, and so forth.'

These types of questions are designed to allow patients to talk about themselves in general terms, and will give indicators as to whether they are potentially stressed, for example in a work situation, or if there are possible difficulties to be faced when they have achieved their therapeutic objective. An example would be if a patient had a problem with confidence and was in an unsupportive relationship.

Current anxieties or potential stressors can now be identified from the feedback given by the patient to the last question:

> 'You mentioned [pinpoint the stressor]; can you tell me a little more?'

These types of questions are used to prompt patients to be able to identify triggers for their condition. It is worth noting that often a patient will have had a condition for some time and will be able to identify when it gets worse, but will not always recognise times when it gets better. Patients do not go for help when they are coping well – so it is legitimate to assume that there will be some additional trigger or stressor which has induced them to take therapeutic action. Suggestions for reducing stress or improving coping strategies may need to be included in the hypnosis script. Another question that is useful at this point, and which will often pinpoint this stressor or trigger is:

'Why have you come for hypnosis now?'
'Is there any particular reason why it has become important for you to deal with this problem now?'

Then any future anxieties of the patient with regard to potential change can be identified. If the patient identifies that there is no particular reason or stressor, this may be a factor in motivation, and an additional impetus may need to be identified:

'What do you want to get out of this process?'

This question can focus the patient's attention on the positive benefits of change.

When taking note of the responses to these questions, the practitioner will also need to be aware of the ways in which the patient is delivering this information. If patients talk about how they feel, or will feel, the suggestions can be delivered using this kinaesthetic emphasis. An example would be the patient who says, 'I want to feel in control,' in response to the above question. The post-hypnotic suggestions should then include suggestions incorporating positive states and feelings as a way of linking in with this. Patients who describe their future states once they have achieved their objective in visual terms will have the suggestions delivered in pictorial form – to 'see' themselves achieving their objective. Lastly, those patients who talk about the future state in auditory terms can have it described back to them in hypnosis in terms of what they may hear when they have achieved their goal, for example hearing positive feedback from people around them who notice the changes in the patient.

More time and emphasis is placed on the patient at this point in the session. The benefits of change are emphasised, rather than the condition, as a way of initiating the required perceptual changes. It is said that a good physician will tell a patient what is right first, then what is wrong – the emphasis is therefore on the positive:

'Tell me a little about yourself'
'Is there anything specific happening in your life at the moment?'

A clear and realistic outcome for treatment will then need to be established. This can be done by applying SMART principles to the objective. SMART stands for Specific, Measurable, Achievable, Realistic and within a given Timeframe. The patient's objective is then evaluated against these criteria. Many patients will have a clear idea or what it is that they do *not* want, and it is often the case that this part of the session needs care as it may be the first time the patient has considered their problem from the viewpoint of a possible solution. The following are example questions that can be used to initiate the idea of looking at the problem from a different angle:

'Tell me specifically what you want out of the process?'
'Describe how things will be different for you?'

Patients will then be able to build up a multisensory image of the way things will be for them when they have achieved their outcome. An example of this would be a person with insomnia, who initially tells the practitioner that they 'want to be able to sleep normally'.

Below are examples of questions which could be used to make the outcome:

• specific: 'Tell me specifically what you mean by a good night's sleep?'
• measurable: 'How many hours' sleep would you need to wake refreshed?'
• achievable: 'How do you think this will happen?'
• realistic: 'How do you expect to be able to do this?'
• timeframe: 'How soon do you want to do this?'

The end result will be an objective fulfilling all of these criteria, which will lend itself to the creation of practical and therefore more readily acceptable suggestions.

Case history

Now that the patient is more comfortable the specifics of the condition can be discussed. The patient will be more relaxed and more willing to provide the information necessary for the practitioner to be able to create unique suggestions. The questions used in this section will be direct, and phrased wherever possible, by using positive language.

Questions which direct patients to recognise what they are already capable of doing are most useful at this point. These are asked to assess motivation and to gain an understanding of the current ego-state of the patient:

'What are you good at?'
'Tell me about some of the things you are proud of?
'What are your achievements?'

The replies can be linked with positive suggestions for change in relation to the presenting condition.

The next stage is to introduce questions on how the patient developed this condition:

'Do you remember when this started?'
'Has there been a time before the condition developed?'

Questions to analyse how patients currently manage their condition can be introduced at this point:

'Has there been a time when the impact of this problem was less than it is now?'
'Do you remember when you were able to cope better?'

The next question:

'Is there anything which you currently do that helps?'

is used in creating positive memory associations when making suggestions. An example would be the patient with tension headaches, who finds that if she lies down in a dark room with her eyes closed the tension begins to ease. Suggestions can be constructed using the idea that whilst in hypnosis she can imagine herself lying down in a darkened room and noticing her tension starting to disappear.

Next, questions to gain an understanding of the interaction between patients and their environment as a result of this condition can be asked:

'How does this condition affect you?'
'What are the symptoms?'
'Does it prevent you from doing anything specific?'
'How do you feel when you [insert condition, for example: have a panic attack]?'

These types of questions will allow the practitioner to gain a deeper understanding of the unique relationship between the patient, their condition and their interaction with that condition. How patients feel about themselves and the condition, and how or if the symptoms create associated behaviours can all be identified at this point.

Rapport

As well as collecting information for use in the creation of the script and selection of the appropriate protocol, the practitioner will also need to demonstrate that they are interested in the patient, and understand their requirements. Rapport in this context denotes the interaction between the patient and the practitioner that makes the patient feel relaxed and able to speak freely about their condition. Rapport is constantly monitored throughout the session. Part of this process will utilise mirroring, pacing and leading patients until they are in a sufficiently relaxed state to enter hypnosis. Mirroring involves the practitioner noting the physical positioning of the patient, for example with folded arms and legs. In simplistic terms, mirroring involves replicating a similar posture and mirroring the ways in which the patient speaks. This is not mimicry – more a modulation of the practitioner's normal way of speaking to make the patient feel that they are dealing with someone similar to them. Leading and pacing involve adopting similar but more relaxed postures and behaviours to lead the patient to a more compliant state. Done well, this process will not be noticed by the patient and will continue throughout the introduction session to a point at which the physical transition into hypnosis is barely discerned by the patient as they will be so relaxed by this time.

Discuss the hypnotic state

Identify any previous experience:

'Do you know anything about hypnosis?'
'Have you ever been hypnotised before?'

This question is asked to allay fears and misconceptions based on that experience. At this point the practitioner should take from patients' previous knowledge or experience of hypnosis (or lack of) and create a model based on what they previously understood, which will reassure them. It is also important that, if a patient has a previous experience of hypnosis which was not a totally positive one, the practitioner needs this information to ensure that they do not accidentally replicate it.

What to expect of the experience

At this point the practitioner will create a model for the patient to describe the events of hypnosis.

Ways in which clinical hypnosis can potentially help

The final part of the preliminary section includes 'selling the benefits of the therapy'. In this section the practitioner will create a further model, including the effects of the therapeutic suggestions, and specifying what input patients themselves will need to add to the process, for example suggestions to *notice* the differences in their skin condition. With this model patients have explained to them, starting with their world view, how, specifically, the clinical hypnosis process will work for them. A good example is patients who identify themselves as being quite analytical; this characteristic can be built in at this point:

'Only the really analytical person will make sure they only take on board suggestions after they have fully analysed them and made sure that they are right for them.'

The aim of this section is to assure patients that this process will not change them as an individual; in fact, it can enhance characteristics which will be useful for them.

Psycho-cybernetics

The final explanation involves describing to the patient a model of the timeframe for change. For this, the model of psycho-cybernetics is modified. It is described to the patient in simple terms that it will take around three weeks for the changes which they have initiated in the session to be fully taken on board by their unconscious processes; in other words, three weeks before they stop being aware of the change. It can be suggested that this occurs during the REM phases of sleep, where the individual reviews new knowledge and learnings from the previous day, and plans the next. In the context of therapeutic change it can be linked to the Emil Coue concept of 'every day in every way you are getting better and better'. Patients will then feel comfortable to self-monitor the changes for a while, and then let go of them as they become accommodated into what the patient considers to be normal.

Last opportunity for questions from the patient

'Any questions before we start the clinical hypnosis?'

Even at this stage there may be patients who have further questions. This gives them a final opportunity to ask them. Patients who are still asking 'What if?' questions, for example 'What if it doesn't work?', at this point may have some secondary gain to holding on to the condition, or may still have some anxieties.

Recapitulate on the objective

At this point the practitioner will run through the SMART goal, and check with patients that they are absolutely clear that this is what they are setting out to achieve. Patients may wish to refine some part of the objective at this point.

A practical point

'Do you need to go to the bathroom before we start?'
'Are you wearing contact lenses?'
'Are you comfortable to close your eyes with the lenses in, or would you prefer to take them out?'
'Is there anything else you need to tell me, for example do you have any hearing problems?'

Statements are then introduced to guide the patient into hypnosis:

'When you are ready to let go of this problem, you can ... start to relax ... '

or:

'You can start by making yourself comfortable, let your arms rest on your lap and place your feet flat on the floor.'

Modulation of voice quality and patterns

The practitioner selects the way in which they will modulate their voice whilst conducting the hypnosis itself, based on the ways in which the patient talks. If the patient is softly spoken, then the practitioner will moderate their voice accordingly during the pre-induction talk. For the patient who speaks louder and more rapidly, the practitioner will replicate this – but, in this instance, will begin to lead the patient to speak more slowly and gently with leading by example.

Induction

The simplest way of selecting an induction is to base the decision on the modality in which the patient currently relaxes. If the patient reads a book or watches television, that is, anything which engages the visual field, a visual induction is appropriate. For patients who listen to music or enjoy social interaction as a way of relaxing, auditory inductions are appropriate. For those who prefer more active forms of relaxation, and engage in physical activities, kinaesthetic inductions are more appropriate.

These are the types of questions to elicit this information:

'What do you do to relax?'

or, for patients who say that they do not relax, do not know how to relax, or who relax by using a 'false friend', such as cigarettes or alcohol, the question can be phrased differently:

'How would you choose to spend a day if you had nothing to do?'

Deepening

Deepening processes can be devised using the modality within which the patient has identified their relaxation state. Those patients who have kinaesthetic ways of relaxing will respond well to suggestions which involve warmth, changing sensations in the limbs, such as heaviness or lightness, and those who include social interaction in their ways of relaxing often respond well to suggestions which include positive emotions or memories. Those whose modality of relaxation is visual can be asked to imagine themselves relaxing, or see their body as it starts to become more limp and relaxed. Auditory patients can be asked to focus on the sound of their breathing as it becomes deeper, or focus on internal sounds such as their heartbeat. The practitioner may also shift the emphasis to the sound of their voice as a sound which will relax them.

Therapeutic suggestions

Therapeutic suggestions need to be:

• phrased positively
• relating to one subject at a time
• SMART.

When therapeutic suggestions are made, rapid eye movement can often be observed as the patient processes the information. These suggestions will consist purely of the patient's objective as discussed in the pre-induction talk and verified before the hypnosis commenced.

Authoritarian versus permissive

The decision as to whether to use a permissive or an authoritarian form of suggestion for therapy can be simply made on the ego-state of the patient (the weaker the ego, the more permissive the suggestions), and also on how the patient describes the way in which they believe clinical hypnosis can help them. An example of the different ways of describing their belief structure can be seen in these statements: 'I just want to be told that I will sleep through the night' or the patient who says, 'I think that it might be quite nice if I could get some rest for a change'. One is direct, the other more passive. The delivery of suggestions needs to be congruent with the patient's approach to the process of hypnosis itself.

Ego-strengthening suggestions

The modality to base the ego-strengthening suggestions can be taken from the section when the practitioner asked about success states. The rationale behind this is to reawaken in patients an awareness that they have succeeded in the past. By using the modality in which they described their successes, whether auditory, visual or kinaesthetic, patients will be stimulated to think in a similar manner. To make the link between past success and future achievement, the two events can be linked together using a linking expression. For example, '*You can feel* as in control in your driving test [the objective] *as you did* when you sang solo in the choir [the past success event]'. As the purpose of ego-strengthening is to reinforce the therapeutic suggestions and generally to make patients feel more positive about themselves, the delivery of suggestions can be more upbeat and motivating to reflect this.

Awakening

Any suggestions which were purely for the purpose of the hypnotic event are to be removed at this stage, for example heavy and tired limbs. In the awakening, suggestions for amnesia may be made. This is appropriate when patients have recurrent patterns of thought, feeling or behaviour which appear to hold them back from making the change. There are many amnesia scripts available; an example of the type of suggestions could be:

'When you remember that there are many things which you have already forgotten, then you may forget those things that it is no longer appropriate for you to remember.'

There will often be an element of confusion in amnesia scripts, allowing analytical patients to analyse the amnesia suggestions, whereas the post-hypnotic suggestions which the practitioner wishes the patient to 'forget' consciously, will bypass the critical faculty. When patients then carry out the post-hypnotic suggestions they will feel that they are making these changes for themselves, rather than having had them imposed upon them.

Post-hypnosis

From this point, the following suggestions and statements are made in the post-hypnosis session once the patient has been fully awakened.

The first task post-hypnosis is to ensure that the patient is fully re-oriented. This can be detected in the patient's posture, speech, and by the practitioner being able to obtain appropriate eye contact. If the patient is not fully alert, the practitioner will tell them to once again close their eyes, at which point the awakening script will be repeated, this time more emphatically. Once the patient is fully re-oriented, they can be asked:

'How long did that seem since you closed your eyes?'

The patient will often state a time much shorter than the actual time. This acts as a convincer that something unusual has taken place, before asking them:

'Do you have any questions?'
'Is there anything you would like to discuss at this point?'

This gives patients an opportunity to reassure themselves of any event in the hypnosis of which they were not sure, or did not expect. The practitioner will *not* remind them of any of the events which occurred during the hypnosis, as this will only serve to bring the patients' critical faculty to the event. It may even make patients anxious if they did not remember the event as recounted to them by the practitioner. They may start to wonder what else they have 'forgotten', and begin to reject the post-hypnotic suggestions.

Homework

In some of the hypnotherapeutic protocols there will be specific homework for patients to do, such as deliberately blushing or paradoxical advertising where they draw attention to the aspect of their condition which most concerns them, for example their anxiety when giving a speech.

In addition, there are more global statements used to encourage change:

'Do not discuss the process with anyone – today, and preferably not at all'

This will allow the suggestions to be taken on board by the patient during their sleep processing phases. Additionally, if language in the form of speech is not added to the experience, the cortex will not be fully engaged, allowing suggestions to be taken on board at a deeper, limbic level. This statement also has the added effect of ensuring that if patients do have someone who may wish to talk them out of making that change, they can say that they are not allowed to discuss it, and that it is part of the process.

'What is your next goal?'
'Now you have … [insert therapeutic objective, for example stopped biting your nails], what are you going to do next?'

These questions serve the purpose of putting the condition into the past, and also focusing the patient's attention on the next objective, either in the context of the protocol or beyond.

Future sessions

The questions and statements relating to this section will all focus the patient's attention on noticing developments between sessions.

'How do you see yourself differently/think things will be different/want to feel in the future?'
'What do you want to be able to achieve before we have our next session?'

Putting the protocol together

When putting this information all together it is like doing a jigsaw puzzle – the picture forms as it is being done. At one end of the scale there are patients who are analytical in their interaction with their condition, and an analytical approach can be favoured. At the other there are process-based patients, who are purely interested in gaining a remission from their symptoms, and straightforward direct suggestions to this effect can be chosen. In between is a sliding scale of decisions, balancing the needs of the individual, the condition itself and the way in which the patient approaches that condition.

The practitioner will need to take note of which aspect the patient places most emphasis upon when talking, and this is the obvious keystone. Once this is changed, the patient's whole relationship with the condition will shift, and therefore can be controlled and then eliminated. If the patient spends most of their time talking about themselves, this is the aspect that the practitioner can most obviously choose to change, and will select a protocol which influences the self, such as inner child work, ego-strengthening or a dissociation. If the patient's focus of attention is on the condition and its symptoms, a protocol which emphasises changing this area is appropriate – cognitive – behavioural approaches, for example. For a patient whose focus of attention is on achieving the objective, a goal-focused approach is favoured, such as inner game, or solution-focused hypnotherapy. It is the unique interaction of the patient with their condition and the symptoms and effects which will make the decision on which protocol is required. There is no single neat formula. However, if the practitioner listens, observes and prompts where appropriate, the patient will identify the most appropriate approach for them.

The next three chapters take this information and relate it to specific conditions to better recognise where this information fits together to when individualising the hypnotherapeutic protocol.

Chapter 8

Smoking cessation

The following framework is a one-session treatment operating on the basis that smoking is primarily a habit to be broken. The type of general suggestions to be included are highlighted; however, the efficacy of the framework depends on personalising this protocol for the patient. In addition, emphasis is placed on ensuring not only that patients break the habit, but that they remain non-smokers.

The first element of this process to be clear about is that it is rare to meet a smoker who 'really wants to stop'. Those who really want to stop do just that, without help. It is not useful to ask a smoker 'Why do you want to stop smoking?' as they will often explain, in well thought-out and logical terms, precisely why it is not a good time for them to stop. Smokers are very good at justifying their habit. There is also little value in attempting to scare smokers from their habit, they are fully aware of the dangers and still continue. Aversive techniques have low long-term benefits in this situation as smokers already know that cigarettes taste and smell bad. They can, and will, frequently find excuses for continuing their habit. This protocol emphasises stopping smoking as well as making sure that patients do not start smoking again.

Useful models for explaining why hypnosis will help to break the habit

Models for explaining the hypnotic event will be used with all patients. It may also be necessary to put forward a model of how clinical hypnosis will effect the therapeutic changes, specifically in relation to the presenting condition. When patients have failed to make the necessary changes for themselves it is useful to put clinical hypnosis into the context of being a mental amplifier or booster. The hypnosis can be described as a process which enhances their willpower, uses their personal characteristics and puts the information where it needs to be. With all this in place, patients will be able to break their smoking habit and remain non-smokers.

'Can you remember when you first smoked?'

This question establishes if patients have a clear memory of when they first smoked, and their body responded by rejecting that smoke. If they can remember, and most smokers will be able to, it also is used to make patients aware that they are only moments away from being someone who never smoked, that is, moments before they inhaled their first cigarette.

River or canal: brain pathways

Some patients state that they do not think that they can stop smoking. Using this model, it can be explained that the clinical hypnosis session will not stop them smoking, but will reconnect the neural pathways which were in place *before they ever smoked, when their body knew how to enjoy life without smoking*. So the smoker is not going to learn something new, only revert to the behaviour that was in place before they ever smoked.

Conscious logic and unconscious behaviour

The practitioner can explain that one of the main reasons why the patient has not been able to stop smoking before is that they have tried to use their conscious, logical thought processes. This part of their mind already knows how bad it is for them to smoke, but it is not the part of their mind which controls their habit. It is the unconscious part of their mind, the part of their mind which contains memories of being a smoker, and controls unconscious processes such as breathing and heart rate, and, more significantly, their habits – which needs to get the picture that this person is now a non-smoker. The unconscious part of their mind knows all the triggers for smoking, and it in this part of their mind they need to be able to imagine themselves involved in all of those activities, but without a cigarette, and being in control. Hypnosis is described as a process which allows the conscious to relax – while the unconscious part of the mind can take on board the suggestions.

Nicotine withdrawal

Nicotine takes around 48 hours to leave the system, during which time some individuals feel tired, sluggish and irritable. Because their immune system is working hard to eject the nicotine, some people are sometimes more susceptible to infection, and may feel quite ill. This will often give the recidivist an excuse to revert to smoking, by convincing themselves that they 'felt better when they smoked'. Obviously, this is not actually the case, so a model can be used which will explain their situation. A post-hypnosis suggestion that the feelings will only last for a couple of days can be utilised to overcome this. This model will only be introduced to the patient if they describe having stopped before and this has happened to them, or if they express it as a particular concern.

Points for inclusion in the smoking cessation script

The script incorporates the following:

- physical relaxation
- permissive hypnosis
- direct post-hypnotic suggestions
- stress management and ego-strengthening
- distraction
- dissociation.

In addition, there will be post-hypnosis suggestions for homework.

Hypnotic script: physical relaxation

Smokers will often identify that smoking is a form of relaxation for them. They will identify that they smoke as a treat, or a punctuation point between activities, or even as a method of getting away from their desk for a break at work. If this is the case, they will benefit from the physical relaxation of the hypnosis itself. Even if this is not the case, the deepening techniques, which use suggestions of warm, relaxed muscles, are well-received and will also go some way to set up a counterbalance for any expectation of tension or anxiety associated with withdrawal from nicotine. The process should therefore be as relaxing as possible, taking into consideration the ways in which the patient currently relaxes (apart from by smoking). As discussed in previous chapters, the modality chosen for the induction can reflect the patient's preferred method of relaxation, with the proviso that their method of relaxing is not that of smoking!

Hypnotic script: permissive hypnosis

Each smoker will have a different pattern of behaviour, but the reasons for starting smoking are often common. An individual who smokes may associate smoking with rebellion, being more interesting or exciting, or being adult. This goes back to the time when they started smoking when those feelings may have been in place, but are now no longer relevant to their habit. Smokers are also aware of the prohibited nature of their habit and will be used to being told not to smoke, either by people, or circumstances. The net result of this attitude is that no smoker likes being *told* what to do in relation to their habit. As a result, the suggestions made as part of the induction and deepener will be invitations rather than instructions. The individual is encouraged to relax, and it can be suggested to them that they can simply enjoy the relaxation part of the hypnosis, for example 'The more you relax, the more easily you will be able to take the suggestions on board'.

For the patient experiencing the hypnosis, relaxing will then be associated with the suggestions of being a non-smoker.

Suggestions made as part of the induction and deepener can also include phrases which imply the patient does not need to do anything in order to become a non-smoker, thus utilising the individual's inertia, for example:

'there is no need for you to pay close attention to the words that I say ... simply the sound of my voice can help you to relax ... all of the suggestions which will be useful to you will be remembered ... there is no need for you to do anything at all ... just relax.'

Hypnotic script: direct post-hypnotic suggestions

The post-hypnotic suggestions will need to be clear and directive, tailored specifically to the times, moods, places and situations where the patient used to smoke. The practitioner will need to go through patients' smoking habits one by one and suggest that they will have 'no desire to smoke ... [in the specific situation]'. Smoking is one of the few conditions where the SMART criteria are not required. The objective for this patient is to stop smoking, and remain a non-smoker. Anything else will fail. There can be no such thing as a social smoker, or occasional smoker – patients either smoke or they do not smoke. The practitioner will be very directive in suggesting that patients will not be able to trick themselves into smoking:

> 'Now that you are relaxed and can pay all of your attention to breaking the smoking habit ... and remaining a non-smoker ... you can find that you will never trick or fool yourself into smoking ever again ... no matter where you are ... who you are with ... or what you are doing ... '

General suggestions will also need to be made to direct patients' attention away from themselves at these times; these are also necessary to ensure that patients do not persuade themselves to smoke:

> 'Whenever you are in a mood ... or a place ... or a situation where you used to smoke ... you will instantly direct your attention away from yourself ... and become involved in a conversation ... or find your attention drawn away by another thought ... '

In the context of the post-hypnotic suggestions, the practitioner can be more authoritarian and directive than at any other point during the script, as although smokers do not like being told what to do, they do like being told what they *are capable* of doing, such as being in control – or making sure that they do not trick themselves into smoking.

The principal suggestion, and one which the practitioner can mention in the pre-induction talk, amplify in the post-hypnotic suggestions and reinforce during the post-hypnosis feedback, is the suggestion that:

> 'The only cigarette you are not going to have is the first one ... only one cigarette ... and you will be fine with this ... '

This suggestion is effective for all smokers, regardless of their patterns or habits, as when smokers try to think of being non-smokers, they will imagine themselves in future situations where they used to smoke. This creates its own anxiety as they start to feel deprived of all the many cigarettes which they will not be able to smoke in future. This concept of the first cigarette being the only one that they will refrain from smoking breaks this anxiety down – and makes the whole idea of being a non-smoker into a much smaller and more manageable concept.

Identifying the problem

As with other conditions, however, the practitioner needs to focus on which particular aspect of this is most relevant for the patient. There are those for whom stopping is not a problem, and they will talk about having stopped before, often for years – but the problem for them is to remain a non-smoker. For others, they cannot imagine themselves without a cigarette in their hand, and any previous attempts to stop have been short-lived. For these patients, the emphasis in the suggestions is on breaking the patterns of thought and behaviour associated with smoking, and imagining themselves in all of the situations where they used to smoke, but without a cigarette, feeling calm and relaxed.

For patients whose focus is on remaining a non-smoker

'You will be in control … in every situation and mood … and … you may find … as a result of being so relaxed now … you will be more relaxed about other situations too … situations where in the past you might have smoked … but now you are in control … you will be more in control over other situations too … '

With these suggestions the emphasis is on control, relaxation and being aware of their triggers for smoking. Patients can then remind themselves that they are only 'not having this cigarette, the first one,' and they will be able to distract themselves away from the trigger.

For patients whose focus is on breaking the habit

'You will be able to see yourself in the future … calm and relaxed … in the situation where in the past you used to smoke … and you have no desire to smoke … in fact … you are so involved in what you are doing … in what is going on around you … that you forget about smoking … '

Symptoms of smoking

It is appropriate, as with all conditions, for the practitioner to ask whether the patient is experiencing any ill effects from their habit. Some patients will say they are not aware of any. For those who do identify symptoms, such as tiredness or shortness of breath, these symptoms can be incorporated into the post-hypnotic suggestions, for example:

'As a result of the fact that you now no longer smoke … you will feel more energised … able to breathe deeply and easily … just as you are breathing deeply right now … '

For patients who do not perceive any ill effects, suggestions for general health and physical wellbeing should be incorporated. Even if patients are not aware of any symptoms, they need to be directed to notice improvements in their physical health:

'You will begin to notice … that generally you feel more healthy … more able to do things … than you did when you used to smoke … '

What does the patient smoke?

In order to personalise the framework thoroughly the practitioner will need to know what the patient smokes, is it cigarettes, roll-ups, cigars or a pipe, and do they smoke anything other than tobacco. If the latter is the case, the patient will need to be informed that this treatment is to stop them from smoking tobacco in any form whatsoever. They will not be able to smoke marijuana with tobacco anymore as this could lead them back to smoking tobacco in the form of cigarettes. There is no demarcation line, and for smokers who say, 'I would just like to have the occasional cigar/joint', the practitioner has to re-emphasise that there is no middle way with this process – they have to make the commitment to stop completely.

What are the specific habits?

In the case history, the practitioner will need to find out the specifics of the habit. The practitioner can ask patients to describe a typical day of smoking, starting with the first one. This will give the information a structure so that it can be fed back logically during the hypnosis in the order it was delivered by the patient. It is also worth noting times when the patient does not smoke, or think about smoking, and this can be added to the suggestions to reinforce that they already have the capacity to control their habit.

The following suggestion is then given:

'No desire to smoke when [insert situation].'

As well as the patterns of smoking, any other specific triggers will need to be identified, as these can be the reasons why patients might be inclined to talk themselves into smoking.

Physical

There are physical cravings associated by some patients with stopping smoking. When individuals make any change they are more aware of what is going on within, and this self-monitoring, associated with the symptoms of nicotine withdrawal, can cause patients to exaggerate, and, in some cases, misinterpret the internal events. Dehydration is often misinterpreted as hunger, and cause patients to reach for food. Also, when patients are dehydrated they might feel unwell; again, this can cause them to become more anxious and further associate these feelings with breaking the smoking habit. Suggestions in the hypnosis such as 'You can drink a glass of water in the situations where you used to smoke.' prevent the dehydration and also give patients something to do with their hands.

Emotional

Some patients identify that they are more likely to smoke in certain moods than others. In these moods, if positive, patients can be encouraged to imagine themselves in that mood, without a cigarette, and feeling really good about the fact that they are not smoking. If the mood is a negative one, the practitioner can make ego-strengthening suggestions to alleviate this mood, or to give them better ways of managing than reaching for a cigarette.

Mental

For patients who believe that smoking helps them think better, suggestions that include the concept, 'Now you no longer smoke ... you will be able to think more clearly' can be made. It can also be pointed out that once patients no longer smoke, they will find that their memory will also improve as their short-term memory processes are not taken up with processing their smoking habit.

Tragedy cigarettes

Patients who have stopped smoking before will often be able to identify an unexpected trigger – something happens to them where the result is that they feel out of control, and the result is they light a cigarette without even thinking about it. In this instance the practitioner will emphasise that this will not happen in future as they will be 'More in control ... whatever the situation' and 'Smoking would only prevent them from coping well with whatever happens in their lives ... '.

Special occasions

Some patients associate smoking with special events, drinking and socialising, or holidays, for example. In this situation, the post-hypnotic suggestions will include patients being able to perceive themselves in these situations, and having *more* control, being *more* aware to ensure that they do not trick themselves into smoking in these situations. Patients can be encouraged to advertise the fact that they no longer smoke when in these situations as a way of reinforcing their decision.

Hypnotic script: stress management

Occasionally, patients will perceive positive or useful effects from their habit. Patients will state that smoking helps them to relax. Apart from explaining in the pre-induction talk that smoking stresses the system rather than the reverse, installing suggestions to be able to manage stress more effectively will always be part of the session and will be tailored to situations the patient identifies as stressors.

Patients will also often identify that while they smoke they feel unable to do other things, such as getting fit, as the smoking invalidates any positive effects they may have from it. With regard to this, suggestions can be made to make getting fit as their next goal:

> 'Now that you have broken the smoking habit you will be able to go to the gym … and feel fitter and healthier than you have felt in a long … long time.'

Concerns about being a non-smoker are usually of the following types: concerns about stress levels, possible mood swings or putting on weight. If the patient tries to stop and finds any of these situations occurring, this can then become an excuse for reverting to the habit. It does not, however, prevent these situations from occurring once they have gone back to smoking; for example, the smoker who puts on weight once they break the habit does not automatically lose that weight once they start smoking again. For smokers who have this has a concern, the additional suggestions of having more control in these specific situations are made.

The ego-strengthening suggestions will emphasise the concept of the patient being in control regardless of the situation they may find themselves in, and these suggestions can be linked back to situations which patients have mentioned during the case history as being ones in which they are already in control.

Hypnotic script: dissociation

Not always a smoker

Smokers will often associate so strongly with their habit that they cannot imagine life without it, it becomes a way of defining who they are, rather than a behaviour. It can be suggested in hypnosis that for most of the time they are a non-smoker, it is only when a trigger occurs that the smoking part of them is activated. Suggestions of this kind are particularly effective for patients who describe the act of smoking as one which they do without even being aware that they are doing it, that is, purely unconscious, and that often they do not actually want, or enjoy that cigarette. This concept of the smoker as only 'a part of you' if further followed through into the awakening script, with suggestions being made for all parts of the individual to wake up, 'except the part of you that used to smoke'. This expression puts the behaviour expressly into the past.

Post-hypnosis: behaviour modification

A number of additional behaviours, called homework, can be suggested to the smoker once they have been awakened from the hypnosis part of the session. One suggestion can be that for the first few days, the patient can sip on orange juice, especially at times when they would have smoked. This can be linked back to the suggestion that they need to replenish the vitamin C in their body. Another is the suggestion that each time they think about smoking, 'the only thing which will come to your lips is a smile as you can be pleased that you no longer smoke'. Finally, the suggestion can be made that it is better to pick up the phone to speak to the practitioner over the first three weeks rather than to pick up a cigarette. This links with the psycho-cybernetics framework and acts as an interruption of the thought-to-action process of smoking.

Summary

An appropriate model is presented to the patient, depending on their mindset, with regard to breaking the habit. The hypnosis part of the protocol includes relaxation suggestions, incorporates the patient's modality of relaxation to deepen the state, and has direct suggestions relating to the triggers for the habit. In hypnosis, these triggers are fed back in the order in which they were presented by the patient in the case history. Any excuses for maintaining the habit are addressed, and behaviour modification suggestions as well as more appropriate stress management mechanisms are installed. The patient is then woken with full ego-strengthening suggestions which link in with their success states by the use of the same modality, and, finally, dissociative suggestions are made for the patient to leave their smoking habit in the past. Distraction and ego-strengthening is reinforced in the post-hypnosis part of the session, and the patient is dismissed with the suggestion that they have been very successful and can now look forward to achieving their next objective.

Suggested scripts for use with smoking cessation can be found by going to www.thamesmedicallectures.com

Chapter 9

Phobias

Patients with phobias frequently present for clinical hypnosis without a formal diagnosis. Before a session is to take place, the non-medical practitioner will need to know that a visit to a medical practitioner has occurred to ensure that they are treated appropriately. This protocol describes one form of hypno-desensitisation protocol, which can take place in a single, or over a number of, sessions, depending on the severity of the symptoms.

Hypno-desensitisation utilises the well-documented psychological approach of desensitisation, with the additional benefit of the rapid relaxation and heightened awareness of the hypnotic state. A patient is required to produce a hierarchy of anxiety-evoking events, and scale the effect of these events by placing them in a logical order (known as a SUDS scale), itemising the least to the highest anxiety-evoking situation within the framework of their condition. Once the scale is produced, hypnosis is then induced, and a signalling device (IMR in the finger) is installed. The practitioner will then describe the events, commencing with the least anxiety-evoking, and make suggestions of relaxation at each point. Where no or minimal anxiety is experienced, the next event on the hierarchy is presented. Where anxiety is experienced, additional relaxation is suggested, until minimal or no anxiety is experienced. This process is continued throughout the hierarchy.

Identifying the specific objective

Even thinking about their trigger situation can stimulate anxiety for patients with phobias. As a result, patients may never have thought about how they wish to be when they have achieved their objective. The result of this is a patient who consistently tells the practitioner what they do *not* want, such as 'I don't want to be afraid of flying', as opposed to what they *do* want to achieve. It is essential to create a clear image of what the patient is working towards as the objective so that patients will know when they have conquered their phobia. Creating this image in specific, concrete and clearly defined terms will also give the patient a positive association with the phobic situation, that is, their objective.

Case history questions

The history of the phobic response

With a phobia it is appropriate for the practitioner to ask the patient to describe the history of their phobic responses. The key questions are itemised below, as well as the rationale behind them.

Asking when the problem first occurred, will allow patients to identify if they are aware of any initiating event. If this is the case, suggestions can be incorporated into the ego-strengthening suggestions that take place after the formal hypno-desensitisation protocol to recall the patient's appropriate response, which was in place *before* this event:

> 'You may start to find ... as a result of this process ... you will begin to feel as you did before ... and will be able to enjoy all the things you did before ... '

For patients who have no recall of an initiating event, the focus of these post hypno-desensitisation ego-strengthening suggestions will be on using all their senses to imagine themselves experiencing the SMART objective.

Uncovering when this situation went from being manageable to becoming a problem, will identify if there were any external stressors which exacerbated the phobic response. If this is the case, then appropriate suggestions for stress management will be necessary. Additionally, if any secondary gains are in place, they will often be identified at this point.

The last area to identify in this section is to find out what is going on in the patient's life currently. Patients will rarely present with phobias unless there is a situation in place, or a planned future event that requires them to take action with regard to their phobia. The patient who is spider-phobic and has a trip planned to a tropical country, or the patient who is about to lose a partner because they can never go out together as a result of the patient's claustrophobia. These events can be built into motivation and ego-strengthening suggestions, allowing patients to experience in the hypnosis, the positive feelings associated with achievement.

All the information elicited from these questions will give a better overview of the patient's interaction with their condition.

Specific events of a phobic attack

Specific symptoms

The specific ways in which the phobia affects the patient will then need to be pinpointed. This is done most effectively by breaking the symptoms down into groups. This will allow patients to discuss each symptom individually and, as a result, to break the symptoms down into smaller and therefore potentially more manageable, events. The responses identified by patients will be those of the fight or flight response. The important factor is to identify them in the order in which they are experienced by the patient, that is, asking what is noticed first, and then tracing the stages of experience, so the practitioner will interject only to keep the chronology of the symptoms intact. If good rapport is maintained, the patient will remain relaxed. This then becomes a precursor to the hypno-desensitisation as experienced during the hypnotic state. Below are described some of the types of information which patients will give at this point.

Physical

All responses associated with the activation of the sympathetic nervous system, for example sweaty palms, shortness of breath, 'butterflies in the stomach', or an increased desire to urinate.

Emotional

Feelings of panic, fear, anxiety or tearfulness can be described. Anger and frustration can also be symptomatic of the phobic response.

Mental

Patients may describe thoughts of wanting to run away or escape from the phobic experience. These are often accompanied with mental images of losing control.

Variations in response since the condition commenced

Since the patient first developed the phobic response, there will have been times when the response was lessened, or even worse than it is currently. It is valid for the practitioner to ask patients to describe these variations. The practitioner can then use the variations when creating suggestions of ways in which patients will be able to cope better with the events which worsened the phobia, and use the times as which the phobia was less problematic in creating positive associations. These suggestions will form part of the ego-strengthening and motivation suggestions, which come after the formal hypno-desensitisation, and are before, or included in, the awakening script.

Eliciting the information about the specific symptoms will allow patients to break down the phobic responses into smaller and therefore potentially more manageable events.

Useful models for explaining why hypnosis will help to alleviate the phobic response

Learnt response

The practitioner can explain that the phobic response is a learnt response which has become maladaptive. As it is learnt, it can also be unlearnt. If patients can remember how they responded before this, it can be used in creating their objective for therapy. If a patient has no recollection, the practitioner can explain that some phobic responses can be learnt from peers or parents, and so it is not surprising that they do not remember when it started – in fact, it is not even their problem. This example of two possible ways of the practitioner responding, depending on how patients react to the initial question, is a prime example of adapting the protocol to the patient. With each of the responses, that of the patient who remembers being able to use this memory, and that of the patient who does not remember, a model can be created by the practitioner to empower the patient. The explanation of the practitioner will need to be logical and factual. In this way, patients will become more relaxed during the pre-induction talk as the practitioner reassures them that their phobic response can be managed.

Conscious logic and unconscious behaviour

This explanation is similar to that used with smoking cessation, and can be adapted for other conditions. In the instance of phobias, the practitioner can explain that one of the main reasons why patients have not been able to rid themselves of the phobia before is that they have tried to use their conscious, logical thought processes. This part of their mind already knows the appropriate response, but it is not the part of their mind that controls the response. It is the unconscious part of their mind, the part of their mind which contains memories of responding in the inappropriate way, and controls unconscious processes such as breathing and heart rate – and habits – which needs to get the picture that this person is now in control and will respond appropriately to the phobic stimulus. The unconscious part of the patient's mind knows all the triggers for the phobia, and it is in this part of their mind they need to be able to imagine themselves involved in all of those activities, with a relaxed response and being in control. Hypnosis is described as a process which allows the conscious to relax – while the unconscious part of the mind can take on board the suggestions.

The role of the conditioned response in a phobia

When discussing their condition, patients will sometimes react with the phobic responses, for example sweaty palms, shortness of breath. If this occurs the practitioner will use a model which reframes this response. The reframe consists of pointing out to patients that it is good that they are able to experience these responses in the absence of the stimulus, as the fact that they are able to do this demonstrates that they are also capable of doing the reverse. In this case, the reverse will be to experience the stimulus without the response.

Explaining how the hypno-desensitisation will work

Once the general information has been obtained from the patient, it is appropriate to collect specific data which will be used to create the hypno-desensitisation protocol. Before this happens, a full explanation of how the sequence of events will occur during hypnosis is appropriate, so that patients understand why this information is necessary. One of the major components of phobias is a fear of losing control. Hypnosis will therefore be explained to the patient as a process which specifically creates *more* control, and the deeper into hypnosis they go, the more control of it, and the phobia, they will gain.

As part of the hypnosis, patients will be asked to experience the anxiety-inducing situations (stimuli) starting with the least anxiety-evoking. The practitioner will explain that no person can be in two states simultaneously, the hypnosis will keep them relaxed and safe while they experience the stimulus. It can be further explained that when the relaxation is experienced in hypnosis, it progressively breaks the link between the stimulus and their inappropriate response, also breaking down the habitual connection. The practitioner emphasises to the patient that they will control the pace of the hypno-desensitisation, and will be given ways of signalling to the practitioner if they wish to stop, or to continue. Once this explanation has taken place, and the patient has been given an opportunity to ask any questions, then the hypnosis part of the session can commence.

Constructing the hierarchy

The patient will then be asked to describe the sequence of events, or individual stimuli, that provoke their phobic response. The framework of a scale of 0–100 is then described to the patient and this becomes their subjective unit of disturbance scale (SUDS). Zero is described as 'no disturbance' and 100 is described as 'the most disturbance they have ever experienced/could imagine experiencing'. Some practitioners will make a graphic representation to use when working with the patient by drawing a line and placing zero at one end of the line, and 100 at the other. Then they will break the line up with evenly spaced marks with the numbers 10–90 on them (see below)

```
0     10     20     30     40     50     60     70     80     90     100
|      |      |      |      |      |      |      |      |      |      |
```

The patient is then asked to describe the phobic stimuli and place them on the scale depending on how much disturbance they experience when thinking about that event. The practitioner will take note of the modality in which the patient experiences each event in order to feed back within the appropriate modality when presenting the scene in hypnosis. This ensures that the patient will get a clear and rapid image of the event, as they have experience of the modality being active in relation to their condition, for example seeing themselves in a specific situation, or being aware of a sound trigger. It is best to start on the hierarchy with zero rather than 100, and for patients to be guided through the hierarchy by increasing the intensity, proximity or any other variables which can be identified in the images presented by the patient. This then becomes a precursor to the experience which they will have in hypnosis. As with all situations, the practitioner will need to be guided by the needs of the patient. It is essential for the practitioner to refrain from enhancing the images or potential disturbance by adding elements which the patient has not already discussed. An example would be the patient who identifies a picture of one spider as rating zero disturbance, and dozens of spiders in a dark enclosed space with her as 100. To create the hierarchy involves manipulating the number of spiders, taking the spider out of the picture, even making that picture into a moving image, or making the space less enclosed or giving it more light. By doing this, the patient can evolve a progression which stays within the confines of the hierarchy. If the practitioner asks, 'Have you thought about what unit of disturbance you would be at if these spiders were crawling all over you?', this adds another, as yet previously unconsidered, component, inducing more, as yet unconsidered, anxiety. The result of this will be a hierarchy that says more about the fears of the practitioner than those of the patient. The final hierarchy should consist of a sequence of events, evenly spaced throughout the scale, for example, an event which caused zero disturbance, 10, 20, 30 and so on, to 100. If the spaces are not even, then there will be a sticking point when conducting the hypno-desensitisation protocol as the increase in anxiety at this point may be too large for the patient to deal with.

Points for inclusion in the phobia hypno-desensitisation script

The script incorporates the following:

- physical relaxation
- permissive hypnosis
- installation of signalling device
- installation of cue word or phrase for relaxation
- scene presentation
- stress management
- ego-strengthening.

In addition, there will be post-hypnosis suggestions for homework.

Hypnotic script: physical relaxation

For an induction, the modality in which the patient relaxes can be chosen. The practitioner should try to avoid induction techniques which incorporate imagery, as in the context of this protocol, the images will be those relating to the phobic situations. As two opposing states cannot be experienced simultaneously, a deepening technique which incorporates suggestions of physical relaxation is the most productive. A deep physical state of relaxation is required before the therapeutic process can be effectively commenced.

Hypnotic script: installation of signalling devices

Signals are installed in the hypnosis script, and will form a continuation of the deepening process. It is important for the patient to be able to signal to the practitioner non-verbally. A verbal response would engage the conscious processes and often brings the patient out of the hypnotic state, or at least into a less deep experience. The first signal, for patients to be able to indicate when they have the stimulus image clear in their mind is required, and the second is used to indicate how patients are feeling when these scenes are presented. A head-nod is usually requested to indicate when the image is clear, and the patient is then asked to confirm this by nodding their head to show they have understood the instruction. The other signals installed are finger ideo-motor-responses (IMRs), used to indicate 'yes' or 'no' when patients are asked whether they are feeling calm and relaxed once the stimulus scenes are presented to them. The patient is then instructed to confirm these IMRs are in place by the practitioner asking test questions. As the patient will be in a very deep state of relaxation, the response time will be long as the deeper relaxed the patient, the longer it takes for a response to occur.

Hypnotic script: installation of cue word or phrase for relaxation

The next suggestion to be installed is a cue or trigger word which, when said by the practitioner, will recall the deepest relaxation which the patient has experienced as part of the hypnosis script. This word, spoken on the out-breath for the patient, becomes associated with relaxation. An expression such as 'now', 'relax' or 'calm' can be used, spoken slowly and calmly:

'In a few moments time you will hear me say the word ... RELAX ... and whenever you hear me say the word ... RELAX ... you will go so deeply relaxed ... so comfortable and safely relaxed ... that you be able to go as deeply relaxed ... as you are right now.'

This cue word will then be used to relax patients whenever they offer a negative IMR response. This would occur when asked in the script if they feel calm and in control when the phobic stimuli are presented to them and they do not feel in control. The cue word is introduced at this point by the practitioner to take the patient away from their negative response. When the patient shows signs of relaxing (breathing slowing down and becoming more regular, and skin pigmentation becoming more heightened) the same stimulus can then be represented.

Hypnotic script: scene presentation

This part of the script involves firstly reminding the patient what is about to happen, that each of the stimuli scenes will be described to them, starting with the least anxiety-provoking, and that they will be asked to nod their head to indicate that they understand. The practitioner will then begin to describe, using the patient's descriptive modality and terms, the lowest stimulus in the hierarchy. The patient is then asked to indicate using the finger IMRs whether they feel relaxed and comfortable (in which case they indicate 'yes') or they do not (by indicating 'no'). The practitioner will note by observing changes to breathing patterns if the patient is demonstrating signs of anxiety. If the patient indicates 'yes', the practitioner will do simple ego-strengthening to reinforce the progress made, and then tell the patient the next anxiety-evoking stimulus or scene will be described. Again, the patient is asked to indicate by a head-nod when this scene is clear in their mind (rapid eye movement will often be observed at this point), and the IMR indicator of feelings is requested. If the response is positive, and the patient is calm and relaxed, this process will continue all the way up the hierarchy. If, however, the patient indicates with a negative IMR, the practitioner will repeat the cue word, along with suggestions designed to reassure the patient:

> 'RELAX ... go deeply relaxed ... calm and relaxed ... you are in control ... and I want you to know that you are doing really well ... really well ... you can relax now ... '

The silence of the practitioner can also be used along with occasional suggestions to indicate to patients that they are fine and safe. This is done until the patient no longer shows signs of distress. Once the patient has relaxed and calmed down, the same scene that caused the negative response is represented. This time, with the benefit of additional relaxation suggestions, patients should be more able to tolerate the stimulus. If they give a positive IMR, indicating that they are relaxed with this scene, the next-highest anxiety-evoking scene on the hierarchy will be presented, and so on, until the hierarchy is complete.

Hypnotic script: stress management

When an individual suffers from the effects of a phobia, an associated symptom may be general anxiety, and need suggestions to be 'More able to manage stress ... so that no matter what is going on around you ... you will feel in control'. This is particularly relevant to patients who identify a clear link between times when they are under pressure or suffering from stress and a worsening of their phobic responses. It is therefore relevant to incorporate these within the ego-strengthening suggestions delivered after hypno-desensitisation.

Hypnotic script: ego-strengthening

When an individual feels that they cannot trust themselves to respond in the appropriate manner with regard to the phobic stimulus, even though on a conscious level they know how they would like to be, self-doubt can set in. This can affect other areas of the patient's life and they start to suffer from a form of mental paralysis when it comes to making decisions.

When to terminate the hypnosis part of the session before completing the hypno-desensitisation

If patients continue to show signs of distress with a particular scene on three or four consecutive occasions, and the relaxation has failed to elicit a 'yes' response that they are prepared to move on to the next stage of the hierarchy, the practitioner can then ask the patient for a head-nod to confirm that they would like to terminate the session:

'You can let me know … by nodding your head … if you would like to end the session at this point … '

The practitioner will then reassure the patient that they have made excellent progress to reach the stage they have reached, and inform the patient that in the next session 'Not only will you be more RELAXED [or whatever the cue word was] … but you will be able to move further than this time … '

Further suggestions can be made at this point that the benefit of the relaxation from the hypnosis part of the session will continue, and the patient will sleep well as a result of the session, continuing to process the appropriate response in their sleep.

When the patient is fully awakened, the practitioner will describe how far they have progressed up the hierarchy, and continue the ego-strengthening by congratulating them reaching this stage. At this point, the practitioner will describe what is going to happen in the future sessions, explaining that they will start with the last stimulus that the patient found manageable, not the last one they were unable to cope with.

If the patient fails to respond

With a small number of patients, regardless of what the practitioner does to suggest creating a SMART goal, or how much relaxation is given, or time spent on the case history, the patient remains negative about their potential to gain a remission from the symptom. This could be for one of a number of reasons:

- poor rapport between patient and practitioner
- failure to identify the appropriate strategy
- low patient self-esteem and poor coping strategies
- lack of patient motivation to achieve the outcome.

The first two have been discussed elsewhere, but the last component, that of motivation, is interesting in relation to a phobia. The phobic response can be identified as being one which the patient does not want, but there may be secondary gains to maintaining the symptoms. Using a phobia of flying as an example, it might be that the patient can control the actions of partners and family by being unable to get on a plane. If this is the case, it often relates back to the third point raised above: that of low patient self-esteem and poor coping strategies. If the patient fails to respond to suggestions when the practitioner is confident that good rapport is in place, and an appropriate strategy has been identified – then comprehensive ego-strengthening suggestions as a full session should be given before attempting to effect a remission from the symptoms. The patient is then instructed in self-hypnosis as a stress management tool, and informed that they should return to have another try when they feel ready.

Behaviour modification

Suggestions made after the hypnosis will relate to testing their new responses. Patients often come for assistance when they have a specific reason to take control of the phobia; the practitioner can capitalise on this by asking patients to focus on how they will feel once they have flown to Spain, or visited the cinema – whichever specific event as described by the patient will tell them that when they do this thing they will know that they are better. If there is no specific future event to test out the responses, the practitioner can suggest that patients deliberately put themselves into the phobic situation. When individuals do this, they have made a conscious choice to be there, and will already feel more in control. It is important not to leave it too long before testing new responses, usually within a three-week period, whilst they still have the new responses fresh in their mind, as the patient may start to doubt the effects of the hypnosis, and the benefits of the motivation and ego-strengthening section may start to fade. The patient would then begin to avoid the stimulus as before, so setting a date to test out their new responses is advisable. The practitioner can suggest that the patient contacts them to let them know 'just how well they did'. This further builds on the ego-strengthening suggestions in hypnosis.

Summary

The key element in this protocol is the breaking down of the phobia into its constituent parts, the stimuli and the responses. This is done first in the case history by having patients deconstruct their responses. This adds language and therefore cortical activity (or left brain functionality) to the response as a way of redressing the balance, whilst the practitioner reframes these responses into ones which, as learnt, can be unlearnt. The hypno-desensitisation part of this protocol includes relaxation suggestions to counter the physical responsiveness to stress, and presents the stimuli in a safe framework in which the patient retains control by the use of signals. Cue or trigger words are installed to relax patients if they show signs of the phobic response when presented with the stimulus scene, and the scene presentation recommences when the patient signals a positive IMR to each stimulus. The hypnosis part of the session is terminated with stress management and ego-strengthening suggestions. This continues until the hierarchy is completed, or until the patient fails to respond with a positive IMR when a scene is presented three or four times. The session is terminated with ego-strengthening relating to progress made, and the next session will recommence with the presentation of the last stimuli scene that the patient found acceptable. The protocol is complete when the patient is able to respond to the scene which represented 100 on their SUD scale with a positive IMR. Post-hypnosis suggestions will direct the patient to deliberately putting themselves in the way of the phobic trigger, and monitoring their new responses.

Suggested scripts for use with phobias can be found by going to www.thamesmedicallectures.com

Chapter 10

Performance anxiety

The term 'performance anxiety' is used here to describe an inappropriate response to a future event, which in turn prevents individuals from being able to function effectively. The severity of performance anxiety varies dramatically, from a mild experience of the symptoms of fight-or-flight, to a complete avoidance and terror of a yet-to-be experienced event alongside a total inability to act in that event. Any performance requires a certain amount of stimulation of the autonomic nervous system as well as a process of individual preparation. If individuals are too relaxed they may fail to put in the necessary effort to be fully prepared for the event, and this can be a precursor to performance anxiety. Conversely, individuals who worry excessively can feel overwhelmed and produce inertia to act, which in turn prevents appropriate preparation. Either way, the net result is identical, an inability to function appropriately in the event.

The necessity for appropriate stimulation and preparation are a primary consideration in selecting a clinical hypnosis protocol which will stimulate the patient sufficiently, whilst reducing any inappropriate anxiety and still produce sufficient depth of hypnotic state to decondition any inappropriate responses.

There are specific areas to be identified and considered when treating performance anxiety. These areas are presented in no particular order, as this information can be elicited at the appropriate time in the pre-induction talk. Patients may introduce the relevant information during the case history, or they may require prompting. In the latter instance, the practitioner will only ask the questions which are relevant to creating the performance anxiety script. The rationale behind this is that performance anxiety is treated here as a stand-alone event which can occur in individuals who consider themselves to be mentally healthy and 'normal'. These types of individuals will come along for hypnotherapeutic assistance for strategic and practical assistance – rather than 'therapy'. Questions asked that patients may consider to be outside the framework of the specific objective will often irritate and can break rapport between practitioner and patient, and confirm a patient's worst fears of clinical hypnosis – as something within which they will lose, rather than gain control.

The protocol described in this chapter pinpoints the specific requirements of the protocol, as well as giving an overview of the areas which may need to be considered. In the circumstance where the performance anxiety is a symptom of another condition, the practitioner may need to work with the patient to evaluate the specific requirements of the principal condition by applying the SMART principles, and work towards that objective, rather than treating the associated symptom of performance anxiety. Failure to recognise this as a consideration can result in the patient maintaining the performance anxiety symptoms.

An imagined response or a reaction to a past event

When giving the case history, patients will be able to identify:

*   if their current response is one which relates to a specific past event or series of events, or
*   whether their anxiety relates to the fear of the unknown.

When this has been identified, the practitioner can use this information to ensure that, in the former case, suggestions can be incorporated into the script for the patient to be suitably prepared this time, and in the latter, that of a fear of the unknown, the patient will have a more appropriate image of what will occur and be able to pre-empt the fear with a more appropriate response. These suggestions are made in the post-therapeutic suggestion stage of the hypnosis session as part of the ego-strengthening, rather than as a specific component of the protocol.

Symptom manipulation

As a certain amount of stimulation is necessary in any performance, there may be a requirement for the practitioner to make suggestions leaving in place some of the reactions which patients currently perceive as being symptoms of their condition. An example of this is the heart pounding sensation, which some individuals perceive as an unpleasant symptom and as a forerunner to full performance anxiety. The practitioner can make suggestions reminding the patient that the physical events of anxiety and excitement are identical, and that they are to start looking forward to experiencing the pounding of their heart as it now means that something pleasurable and exciting is about to occur. Another way of manipulating the symptom other than through cognition is for the physical awareness of the symptom to be reduced by asking the patient to start to monitor what is going on around, rather than within them. In both instances, symptoms will be reframed as positive and welcome, rather than negative and dreaded.

Symptom manipulation is a component of this hypnotherapeutic protocol, and suggestions which alter the individual's physical and psychological perception of the symptoms in a positive way will serve to reduce anxiety, and encourage patients to experience a positive reaction to the anxiety-evoking event when they experience it in hypnosis. This, in turn, will act as a template for their response when they experience the event later *in vivo*.

Performance anxiety as a stress-related condition

Performance anxiety can often be a reaction to stress. If the patient has poor coping strategies, the condition may remain impervious to the therapeutic process. The practitioner can ask questions which relate to what is happening in the patient's life at this moment to ascertain whether there are additional stressors exacerbating the performance anxiety, and then decide whether there is a benefit in teaching the patient self-hypnosis as a better way of managing their stress.

Additional methods of assisting patients who have poor stress-coping mechanisms may involve reducing the response to stress by direct suggestion or behaviour modification suggestions, or by including some form of reframe of their stress response. An appropriate reframe is for the practitioner to talk of the patient's responses to stress in terms of hypersensitivity rather than a maladaptive mechanism. When patients' responses are presented to them in this way, they can begin to consider the use of clinical hypnosis as a way of 'retraining' their system to respond appropriately, rather than viewing themselves as having a 'problem' or requiring 'therapy'.

Identifying the problem

When individuals present with performance anxiety they will have a unique view of the problem in relation to their performance. For some individuals the performance anxiety becomes an avoidance technique created by low self-esteem, and, at the other end of the scale, there are individuals for whom the desire for a 'perfect' performance creates constant disappointment and therefore a self-fulfilling prophecy of the anxiety-evoking event or events. If patients consider these aspects of the condition to be relevant, the practitioner may ask what, specifically, the patient requires of the protocol, that is, if they feel that it is necessary to deal with these aspects of their cognition in order to gain a remission from the condition. If the patient wishes to explore these aspects and a SMART objective can be obtained, the practitioner will work with this. Often, the performance anxiety will reduce as a result. The associated behaviour may still need to be addressed as a separate issue as it may have become an habitual response. In summary, identifying the problem involves identifying which aspect of the performance the patient perceives to be the problem, and recognising the significance of this aspect in relation to the whole performance. An example would be the athlete who can consistently run at a specific rate when in training, but fails to do so when placed under race conditions.

Identifying the symptoms

When taking the case history the practitioner will need to discover the specific symptoms and the order in which patients experience them – from the first identifiable reaction, through each additional response. These symptoms may be physical, mental or emotional in varying combinations at different times during the performance. Patients will often find it initially quite difficult. As they start to do this, they are breaking down what had been a global reaction into a sequence of smaller, and therefore potentially manageable, responses, and it will become easier for them to describe their reactions. This sequence of events will be fed back in the order in which they have been presented while the patient is in hypnosis, with the additional overlay of the previously identified symptom reframe. It is also relevant to identify if there is a point in the escalation when the patient feels the symptoms become unmanageable. An additional suggested trigger for being in control can then be suggested to the patient. This control trigger can be linked to a past experience which the patient has identified as being one in which they recognise as within their control.

An example of this process would be:

> 'When you notice your heart starting to accelerate [first symptom] ... so you can begin to feel excited [symptom reframe] ... as excited as you were when you first experienced driving your car on the motorway [control trigger].'

This collection of suggestions should be made for the first trigger and for any subsequent triggers where the patient notices an escalation of the responses. There may also be a point at which the patient felt they moved from feeling in control, to feeling that they no longer had control of their response. This stage is particularly significant, and suggestions should be concentrated in this area using the framework outlined above, as well as additional ego-strengthening suggestions which are designed to help the patient retain perspective. When observing patients' body language when these suggestions are being made, the practitioner will be able to identify if the suggestions are sufficient, or whether additional relaxation suggestions will also need to be made. This can be evaluated from observing any signs of discomfort or anxiety displayed by the patient.

Identifying the effects of the condition

As already mentioned, the performance anxiety may, in some instances, be a symptom of a broader condition, either one of stress, or when patients feel out of control in another area of their lives, and this has translated into performance anxiety. It is valid for the practitioner to ask whether patients wish to participate in this performance. If their motivation is low, for whatever reason, the objective of reducing the performance anxiety will also be a low priority. Motivation is a key factor in creating and perpetuating new patterns of thought, behaviour and emotions in clinical hypnosis. In addition, patients may have specific secondary gains which they will identify in the case history. This happens when patients describe the reasons why, specifically, they have not already let go of this problem, or indeed, why they will find it difficult to change at this time. If this occurs it is worth considering that the symptoms have some value for the patient which they are not prepared to discard, or have not found a more appropriate replacement. For each individual to be appropriately motivated there will have to be an identifiable benefit to the patient to counterbalance any benefit which resulted from maintaining the symptoms. If this is the situation, the practitioner will need to incorporate further suggestions. These suggestions can take the form of a thought, feeling or behaviour which brings equivalent, or additional, benefit compared with any benefits that are to be discarded by the patient.

Identifying the specific triggers

When patients discuss the problem they may identify specific external triggers. These will be in addition to the triggers created by the heightened awareness of their internal responses. These triggers may be sounds, visual or physical triggers. Examples of each could be the sound of an audience, or the look on another person's face, or the touch of their hand on the door handle as they prepare to enter a room. These triggers can then be incorporated into the script as cues for setting off a different response or sequence of responses:

> 'As soon as your hand grasps the door handle [external trigger] ... you can notice your heart beating more quickly [internal response previously feared] ... you will begin to feel excitement [reframe of internal response] ... '

As you can see from the example above, it is more appropriate to retain the internal response and reframe it. This acknowledges the requirement for a certain amount of adrenal response in the performance whilst moving the awareness from fear to pleasant anticipation of its occurrence.

Identifying the objective

With performance anxiety, the objective can be made subject to SMART goals. The objective will also incorporate how the patient is going to feel once the objective has been achieved, and those feelings are incorporated into the ego-strengthening section:

> 'When you have passed your driving test [SMART goal] ... you will feel so proud [feelings of achievement previously identified].'

Useful models for explaining why hypnosis is effective with performance anxiety

As with all other conditions, it is key to patients' motivation and compliance with therapeutic suggestions that the hypnotic procedure and the therapeutic suggestions are explained in a way that will encourage them to experience both fully. When explaining why and how the clinical hypnosis will influence performance, it is often valid to describe the natural responses to performance itself. This will allow individuals to understand how their reaction has developed. This is particularly useful for the analytical individual who requires some form of rationale to comprehend their responses. As with all of these types of descriptions for hypnosis and clinical hypnosis, they are designed specifically to fit into the mindset of the patient, enhance the positive expectations of the therapeutic process, or reduce or eliminate the patient's negative response to specific triggers.

Explaining fight or flight

A simple explanation of the fight or flight response (*see* Chapter 2, the section on stress management (p. 12) and Appendix II, 'Glossary of terms' for more information) is valid in the context of performance enhancement. Once it is explained to individuals that their response is a natural one that has simply failed to complete, the emphasis on the problem shifts from being one that is out of their control, into one which requires completing rather than changing.

Conscious logic and unconscious behaviour

This is another adaptation of the model seen in smoking cessation and in phobias. In the instance of performance anxiety, the variation centres on the model of the system being appropriately prepared for the performance. In this context, the practitioner can explain that one of the main reasons why patients have not been able to rid them-selves of the performance anxiety before is that they have tried to use their conscious, logical thought processes. This part of the patient's mind already knows the appropriate response, but it is not the part of their mind which controls the response. It is the unconscious part of their mind, the part of their mind which contains memories of responding in the inappropriate way, and controls unconscious processes, such as breathing and heart rate – and habits, which needs to reconnect with the appropriate response. Hypnosis is described here as a process allowing the conscious to recognise the responses as appropriate (such as increased heart rate and so forth), whereas the unconscious part of the mind can take on board the suggestions, allowing the individual to be part of the event rather than predicting how they will respond.

Can you remember when you first had this inappropriate response?

If patients can establish when they first had the inappropriate response, this information can be incorporated into the suggestions in two ways. The first is for suggestions to revivify in hypnosis how patients responded moments before they first experienced the negative response, or for suggestions to be made that in hypnosis patients can regress to their natural response, and bring this into the present. The aim of this question is to establish that the patient is going to learn how to respond in a way which they already have in place, but have forgotten – rather than learn a new response. Patients whose performance anxiety is based on a real past event can usually recall the time of origin. Patients for whom the performance anxiety is more of a fear of the unknown will often fail to do so.

Points for inclusion in the performance anxiety script

The script incorporates the following:

- patient modality of relaxation
- cue or trigger words

- performance anchor
- de-sensitisation
- learning self-hypnosis
- ego-strengthening.

In addition, there will be post-hypnosis suggestions for homework.

Modality of relaxation

As performance anxiety is one of the conditions that is influenced by stress, individuals will often express that they are not doing anything to relax at the moment, or that they feel unable to relax. Identifying what they used to do, or would like the time to do, or even to ask them to imagine that if they had a day off from all this worry, how they would choose to spend their time, will help identify an appropriate modality for the induction. When a modality is selected which the patient already associates with a relaxation state it will enhance their capacity to enter hypnosis.

Cue or trigger words

As part of the deepening process, cue or trigger words need to be installed. These words are suggested as cues for patients to experience deep, rapid relaxation, as well as positive states. Once installed, these words can be repeated during the post-hypnotic suggestions at times when patients have identified increased awareness of their anxiety. These words are simple instructions, such as 'relax', 'calm' or 'now', and can also be used by patients in their self-hypnosis as reinforcement. The phrase 'as soon as' is also useful as a cue for the practitioner to be able to install appropriate responses within the context of the performance:

> 'As soon as you walk into the room where you are to give the talk [external cue] ... calm and relaxed [cue for positive state] ... '

Performance anchor

In creating a positive future template for the performance, it is useful to use cues. In this instance, the cues need to be actions which the individual must undertake as part of the preparation phase of the performance. This could include turning the key in the ignition in a driving test scenario, or putting on a specific item of clothing for an actor about to go on stage. When this action is linked to a positive state, it will become a performance anchor. Suggestions are made that the patient will:

> '... feel ... [required state, for example confident] ... as soon as you ... [action, for example first walk out onto the stage].'

Once these positive feelings are linked to the action, the patient can reinforce this in their mental rehearsal, or as part of any self-hypnosis undertaken.

De-sensitisation

Individuals with performance anxiety can become overly sensitised to their environment and to any self-monitoring which goes on. The result of this is that they predict what they believe other people are thinking, and become increasingly self-critical. The de-sensitisation suggestions relate to creating a much more realistic perception of the event. De-sensitisation can be done as part of the therapeutic suggestions:

> 'You will become so involved in what you are doing that you forget about yourself … and become fully involved in what you are doing.'

In this way patients are encouraged to refrain from a focus on their environment, or other people's thoughts and actions, and also away from the excessive self-monitoring which previously caused additional anxiety. This aspect of the performance enhancement protocol is particularly important to include for those individuals who can perform when there is no audience, or who feel that their performance is not being critically judged. In these situations, the de-sensitisation process can include suggestions that the patient will be able to experience the positive experience of the event:

> 'You will be so focused on what you are doing … that you become unaware of your surroundings.'

Learning self-hypnosis

For patients with performance anxiety, learning self-hypnosis fulfils a number of requirements. First, it allows them to mentally prepare for the event whilst in a relaxed and focused state. Second, it can be used as a stress management technique, and as a behavioural prescription where the patient can reinforce suggestions made during the clinical hypnosis session, and further supplement them with positive suggestions of their own.

Mental preparation or mental rehearsal

As part of this process, patients will be asked to discuss the practical preparation they have undertaken for the performance. If this includes actual or mental rehearsal of the event, the practitioner can ask whether the outcome of the event, when rehearsed, is a positive one. If this is the case then the patient will be encouraged to supplement this rehearsal whilst in hypnosis, where they can experience as many positive variations of the event as they wish. If the patient is aware that their rehearsal includes a negative outcome, the practitioner will, when teaching the patient self-hypnosis, make suggestions containing the SMART goal already set, which will be reinforced at this point.

Stress management

General responses to stress or coping mechanisms can also be addressed as part of this process, particularly if the performance anxiety is symptomatic of a wider inability to manage stress appropriately. The self-hypnosis then becomes a method of relaxation, rather than one of auto-suggestions for change. The benefits of this will come to the patient in improved sleep patterns and an increased perception of control as they start to create a habit of using the self-hypnosis as a method of relaxation.

Ego-strengthening

Ego-strengthening is an essential component of this protocol. Individuals who suffer from performance anxiety will often experience periods of generalised self-doubt. By reminding them of those things that they have already achieved by the use of suggestions which recall past positive experiences, and by future orientating them to the time when they have experienced the success associated with a positive performance, the patient will be placed in a positive state. This then allows patients to remain involved in what they are doing, rather than observing it, or predicting their possible performance. Non-specific ego-strengthening is also appropriate, with suggestions that the patient can feel more confident and motivated generally.

Other aspects for consideration

As well as the specific requirements of the protocol there are other areas outside of which note can be taken, and suggestions incorporated as appropriate.

Has anything worked for the patient before?

If this is the case, suggestions which remind patients of the effect can be included in the script.

Why is it important to deal with it now?

A significant current or future event is often the impetus for individuals to seek help. It is rare for a person to present with performance anxiety where there is not a requirement for them to experience the trigger. An example would be in the case of public speaking, where the patient has been told that they have to give a speech at a wedding, or the premature ejaculator who has entered a new relationship which is about to progress to a level of intimacy. Obviously, the fact that there is a future event to base additional anxiety upon creates its own stress, with the individual becoming increasingly disturbed. The result of this can be an escalation of the anxiety into other areas of the individual's life. When the practitioner asks questions to uncover whether there is a specific future event in place at which the patient feels they are going to be subject to the performance anxiety, this can be included as part of the ego-strengthening. Individuals can be future-oriented into an image in which they can experience the event in a positive manner. Feelings of achievement from beyond the successful completion can be incorporated into this image and used to further motivate the patient.

Dissociated states

There are occasions when patients will discuss the event in a dissociated manner. They may talk of 'a part of them that feels anxious' or, when describing the event, speak of themselves in the third person, or as an observer rather than participant. If this is the case it may be appropriate to include a dissociation protocol before de-conditioning the performance anxiety using the protocol described in this chapter. The objective of this would be to get the part of the individual which experiences the anxiety back under conscious control, before dealing with the symptoms of performance anxiety.

Another aspect of dissociation can be utilised as part of the awakening script, where the part of the individual experiencing the performance anxiety can be put to rest, and a positive, confident part brought into play:

> 'In a few moments' time ... I will wake you ... you will hear me count from one to ten ... and by the count of eight your eyes will open ... and by the count of ten you will be fully wide awake ... all normal sensations will return to your limbs ... every part of you will be back in the present ... except the part of you that used to be anxious when you [performance] ... that part of you can rest ... remain in the past ... and in the place of this part of you ... a confident ... relaxed part of you can wake ... and ... whenever you are in ... [performance situation] ... you will be confident and relaxed ... so ready ... one ... two ... '

Post-hypnosis

After the hypnosis is concluded, patients will be encouraged to demonstrate their ability to do self-hypnosis. This will allow them to ask any questions and check that they are doing it correctly. Instructions are made by the practitioner as to how often the patient should do their self-hypnosis. Once during the day, and just before they go to sleep at night will be sufficient, as well as instructing patients that it will be fine if they wish to do it more frequently.

The patient will be reminded by the practitioner of the instructions suggested in the hypnosis. This is done to reinforce the suggestions, and remind patients of any suggestions that they may not have heard. The concept of 'act as if' can be introduced in the post-hypnosis session. This is where patients are encouraged to try out their new behaviour as if they could already do it.

Paradoxical advertising

Lastly, one of the simplest and most effective ways of reducing anxiety associated with a future event is to advertise that anxiety. If the patient has a fear that people might notice that they are anxious, suggestions can be made which give the patient the confidence to advertise that fear to those people whom they fear might notice. In doing so, the patient is taking control of one element of the performance. The more control which the patient can take in that event, the less stress they will experience, directly reducing the effects of the anxiety.

Summary

Using clinical hypnosis to reduce performance anxiety includes initially creating an appropriate model for understanding the patient's condition and the way in which this process can assist in making changes. Once this is established, a hypnotic process which allows the patient to relax as part of the induction and deepening process is utilised to reduce stress and create a physical state which is in opposition to the anxiety state previously experienced as part of the performance. Then the emphasis in the hypnosis moves to creating a focused, motivated and confident state in which cues direct suggestions for more appropriate thoughts and behaviour within the context of the performance itself. The patient will then have a template for the performance in which they are experience a positive outcome for the event. This is reinforced by the use of self-hypnosis and, if appropriate, paradoxical advertising.

Suggested scripts for use with performance enhancement can be found by going to www.thamesmedicallectures.com

Conclusion

Clinical hypnosis as a process cannot be neatly categorised. This volume is not comprehensive and each chapter could take up a book on its own. It has attempted to give an overview of the form and content of clinical hypnosis sessions, and set out some of the variations relevant to patients' interactions with their condition. It is these variables that make each session with a patient unique.

As this volume has set out to demonstrate, the practitioner needs to listen and observe, demonstrate rapport and create confidence in the process before setting out to use the hypnotic state to fully facilitate this change.

These skills can be transferred to any form of communication with another individual, and it is always worthwhile remembering that just as we are observing others, so they are taking note of the things we say and do. An understanding of these skills will make the individual think more – and often say less.

In Appendix III are details of websites to explore for further knowledge about this fascinating subject.

I hope you have enjoyed this volume.

Ursula James
ursulajames@thamesmedicallectures.com

Appendix I: A brief history

This list is not a complete account of all who have used or studied hypnosis or hypnotic phenomena. In this section, only specific events and individuals are mentioned whose innovations and contributions changed the perception or use of clinical hypnosis, or are relevant to the medical applications of this tool.

Before Mesmer

From ancient Egypt, through to Roman times and beyond, the use of suggestions made by an authority figure while the recipient was in a sleep-like state has been recorded. In the healing temples of Aesculapius, the Greek God of Medicine, the priests would walk among the patients as they slept, giving suggestions of health and wellbeing, which would be interpreted as the gods speaking to them in their dreams.

In many cultures throughout the world, shamans, wise men and healers use the power of words and ritual from an authority figure, associated with the expectations of their followers, to 'heal'. The terms 'cure' or 'healing' are not in the vocabulary of clinical hypnosis, although there are similarities and overlapping experiences even in mainstream medicine, where, for example, words heard by a patient in surgery can be related back postoperatively.

Father Gassner

The first name in modern history associated with the use of a hypnotic state is the Catholic priest, Father Gassner. He theorised that patients who suffered ailments with no obvious origin were possessed by the devil and needed to undergo a ritual to be freed. This ritual took the form of being touched by a crucifix, where the patient would then fall in a faint-like state, where suggestions for casting out the devils and resuming their normal behaviour would be made. This sleep was termed 'death', from which the power of Christ through Father Gassner would help them to be 'reborn' cured from their ailment. Father Gassner would allow observers to watch this ritual, among them, Franz Anton Mesmer.

Mesmer, Franz Anton (1734–1815) and animal magnetism

Mesmer theorised that disease was the direct result of an imbalance of a magnetic fluid. This fluid could be influenced by a process of redistributing this universal fluid, known as 'animal magnetism'. During this process a 'crisis' was suggested to the patient, wherein they experienced pseudo-epileptic seizures and a remission of the neurotic symptom. The 1784 French Royal Commission studied these events and came to the general conclusion that the results were attributable to the suggestions and imagination of the patients rather than to any magnetic force. Mesmer's theories were then discredited.

Puysegur, Marquis de (1751–1825)

A student of Mesmer, de Puysegur continued Mesmer's work. He ceased suggesting the 'crisis' that was so central to Mesmer's process, and it ceased to occur. He discovered that patients fell into a sleep-like state (somnambulism) where they experienced amnesia of trance events and became highly responsive to suggestions. Puysegur concentrated on the following aspects of this suggestive state: the focus of attention, the heightened acceptance of suggestions, and the amnesiac state of hypnotic events as experienced by subjects.

Abbe de Faria

De Faria gave demonstrations of animal hypnosis where hypnotic phenomena such as hallucinations were observed.

Braid, James (1795–1860)

Braid coined the term 'neurypnosis', soon shorted to hypnosis. He initially theorised that the somnambulism discovered by de Puysegur was caused by paralysis of the nerve centres. Braid went on to observe that hypnotic trance could be induced by the fixation of attention on a fixed object, for example a watch. He also demonstrated that patients could be re-hypnotised by a single stimulus, such as a word. He later concluded that hypnosis was caused by concentrating the attention on one idea (monoideism) rather than a physiological process. Pavlov later expanded on these theories of neural inhibition in his concept of sleep states as a form of progressive cortical inhibition.

Elliotson, John (1791–1868)

His belief was that hypnosis should be thoroughly researched, and that it was the responsibility of the medical profession to conduct that research. In 1846, he founded the first hypnosis Journal, *Zoist*, which published research on the use of hypnosis with a wide range of medical conditions. When he chose hypnosis as his subject for the Harveian Oration in 1846, he was discharged from University College Hospital as a result.

Esdaile, James (1808–1859)

Esdaile specialised in hypno-anaesthesia (mesmeric sleep) and performed hundreds of operations in India using hypnosis as the only anaesthetic. When placed in charge of a hospital near Calcutta he continued his research into the use of hypnosis in surgery, only to be overtaken by events when the anaesthetic properties use of ether and chloroform were discovered in 1853. He published a number of volumes, among them *Hypnosis in Medicine and Surgery* (originally entitled *Mesmerism in India*). In 1891 the British Medical Association reported the 'as a therapeutic agent, hypnotism is frequently effective in relieving pain, procuring sleep and alleviating many functional ailments'. This is considered to be a direct result of Esdaile's work in the field.

Charcot, Jean-Martin (1825–1893)

Charcot was a neurologist at the Salpetriere neurological clinic, who theorised that hypnosis and hysteria were both symptomatic of disorders in the central nervous system. He believed hypnosis to be a pathological state that weakened the mind and could only be experienced by hysterics. He concluded that hypnosis was an induced seizure when his hysteric patients showed epileptic-like symptoms when they were in a trance. Renowned for his work in various aspects of medicine, his reputation was undermined when this theory was disproved by the work of Liebault and Bernheim.

Liebault, Ambroise-Auguste (1823–1904)

A student of Charcot, this physician focused on the importance of the use of suggestions in creating a hypnotic state, and was the first to formally observe the subjective nature of hypnotic phenomena. He concentrated on rapid hypnotic techniques (such as the use of the word 'sleep', with a hand pass to induce trance), and did not consider deep trance states to be a requirement for therapeutic change.

Bernheim, Hippolyte (1825–1893)

Professor of Medicine at the University of Nancy, a student of Liebault, Bernheim too concentrated on the importance of the use of suggestions in creating a hypnotic state. He theorised that patient expectation of trance events would influence their suggestibility, and that hypnosis was part of ideo-motor action influenced by suggestion. This school of thought focused on hypnosis as a psychological process where suggestions were central, and the hypnotic ritual element was minimised. Bernheim's major contribution to the history of hypnosis is primarily in publicising the use of hypnosis to a wider audience.

Breuer, Josef (1842–1925)

Breuer was the first to formally use hypnosis for the use of conditions other than pain alleviation. Breuer's work initially attracted Freud to the use of hypnotic techniques. This is documented in the case of Anna O, which led to a change in emphasis in the use of hypnosis from direct suggestions to alleviate symptoms, to the use of hypnosis for uncovering the origin or cause of the symptom (hypno-analysis).

Janet, Pierre (1859–1947) and Freud, Sigmund (1856–1939)

Janet and Freud worked together observing the effects of hypnosis, out of which Freud went on to create 'free association'. This was from observing the random, dream-like quality of comments made by hysterical patients as they experienced the hypnotic state, or post-hypnotically. Freud theorised that the hypnotic state was not essential to the recovery of the patient, whereas Janet went on to work with the framework of the 'dissociated self' as a therapeutic technique within hypnosis.

Bramwell, John Milne (1852–1925)

Author of *Hypnotism: It's History, Practice and Theory*. He is best known for his work with hypnosis in medicine and surgery, having learned of hypnosis through the work of James Esdaile.

Coue, Emile (1857–1926)

The pioneer of positive self-suggestion as a way of achieving wellbeing and mental health, he is best known for his phrase 'Every day in every way I am getting better and better'.

Moll, Albert (1862–1939)

A contemporary of Bramwell, Moll wrote *Hypnotism* in 1889, the legal aspects of using hypnosis, how the waking state differs from a hypnotic state, and made the first reference to 'waking hypnosis'.

World War I

The First World War had an impact on the way in which hypnosis, psychiatric definition of conditions and treatment were viewed and conducted.

As soldiers began to return from the trenches displaying symptoms which became known as 'battle fatigue' and, more recently, have been termed 'post-traumatic stress disorder' (PTSD), the classification of mental illness and treatment had to be rapidly reappraised. One of the results of this reappraisal was the development of a regression technique (hypno-analysis) by Dr Hadfield in the UK to uncover these traumatic memories to produce a cathartic outcome. The psychiatric profession became interested in the use of hypnosis at this time because of the potential for rapid improvement. Once again, before thorough research could be undertaken, the use of pharmacological agents became the major treatment of choice.

After World War II

It was not until 1955 that the British Medical Association officially recommended that medical schools add hypnosis to their curriculum. In 1958 hypnosis was first taught to practitioners in France as part of their medical education.

Erickson, Milton (1901–1980)

An American physician, known as 'the father of modern-day hypnosis', Erickson conducted numerous clinical and experimental studies which evaluated the nature of trance, trance logic, the use of specific language, the use of metaphor, the role of the patient in creating hypnotic states and hypnosis as an inner-directed altered state of consciousness. He is best known for the use of indirect suggestions and communication as a means of therapeutic strategy. Within this, Erickson utilised the concept of unconscious search processes whereby the mind seeks the answer to a question from within. On that basis, the individual created the problem; they already have some idea about how to resolve it.

His work led to a number of developments, some of which concentrated on one specific aspect of his work. Examples include:

- Earnest Rossi – hypnotic theories.
- Jay Haley – strategic models of therapy in hypnosis.
- Richard Bandler and John Grinder – neuro-linguistic-programming (patterns of language and communication).

With neo-Ericksonian approaches the general emphasis is on:

- the patient's ability to access appropriate methodologies for change by creating an appropriate internal environment
- the use of indirect suggestions.

White, Robert (1904–2001)

In his *A Preface to the Theory of Hypnotism* White put forward the theory that hypnotic experience and therapeutic change requires the patient to be creative. Therefore hypnosis was more closely related to goal-driven processes than purely neurological or physical events. Sarbinin expanded on this theory of hypnosis to encompass the event as a social encounter involving role-play.

Research and development

Research into the medical applications of hypnosis really began in the 1950s and 1960s with individuals such as TX Barber, ER Hilgard, MT Orne, TR Sarbinin, J Hartland and D Elman. Since then, clinical hypnosis has been introduced into medical training programmes in the USA, France and Germany. It has yet to be brought into the mainstream medical education in the UK, despite the BMA recommendation of 1955 that it should be taught. The University of Oxford Medical School was the first medical school in the UK to offer a clinical hypnosis module as a special study option within its undergraduate programme in 2002, taught by the author, and she has since introduced it in a further seven UK medical schools.

Modern hypnosis

The modern uses of hypnosis have themselves become as polarised as the figures from its history. The Theosophical Society, charismatic healing, stage hypnosis and advertising, all use elements that stem directly from Mesmer.

Appendix II: Glossary of terms

Reproduced with kind permission of its author – Tom Connelly, Secretary of the British Society of Clinical Hypnosis.

A

Aesthesiogenic
Sensations of a sensory nature produced by suggestion.

Agnosia
Condition where patient is unable to correctly interpret sensory impressions.

Alexia
Inability to recognise the written word as words. This condition is often the result of a brain lesion but can be caused by suggestion.

Amnesia
The loss of memory, partial or total, often caused by shock or trauma. Can be due to physical causes, can be caused by suggestion. Sometimes occurs spontaneously after arousal from hypnosis.

Analgesia
Reduction or loss of the sensation of pain, which can be achieved through hypnosis.

Anchorages
Frames of reference which people use to make further judgements.

Anchoring
The technique of associating several 'keys' with one fixed point of reference, with the idea of using those keys to later evoke that fixed reference. Form of conditioning by association of ideas. Used in NLP and clinical hypnosis.

Anaesthesia
Loss of sensation and sensitivity, usually due to chemical agent (as with surgery) but is also an important phenomenon of deep hypnosis. Hypnosis can be used as an anaesthetic and many instances of its usage are on record.

Animal magnetism
A term coined by Franz Anton Mesmer (1734–1815), who theorised that the effects of 'hypnotism' (which was then to be called 'Mesmerism' after him and before that time known as 'Charming') were due to a fluidic magnetic medium that could be passed from person to person.

Aphasia
Loss of the ability to speak, usually through non-physical causes and typically a symptom of hysteria. Can also be produced by hypnosis (without the presence of hysteria). Can also be caused by lesions of the brain (cortical).

Aphemia
Inability to speak certain words.

Atavistic theory
The theory proposed by Ainslie Meares MD to explain the phenomenon of hypnosis. He posited that in hypnosis the higher centres of the brain are systematically closed down and access is gained to parts of the brain which are primitive and pre-rational. Thus hypnosis could be explained as a form of regression to pre-critical functioning.

Attention
The ability to sustain one's awareness by focusing it on a particular thing.

Auto-hypnosis
Where a patient has learned the ability to place himself in a state of hypnosis.

Autogenic
Relating to things which originate within the self.

Autonomic
Self-directed, independent.

Autonomic nervous system
The nervous system responsible for many of the body's functions, particularly those of the glands, the smooth muscles, respiration and circulation. It is located along the spine and cerebro-spinal system and is completely efferent in function. It is reactive and responsible for the 'fight or flight' response.

Auto-suggestion
Suggestions which originate from within the self.

Aversion
A strong dislike of something.

Aversion therapy
A form of deconditioning by associating something unpleasant with a particular behaviour pattern you are trying to eradicate. Typical of behaviour therapy it is

used sometimes in hypnosis, for example, to associate a foul thing (like dog excrement or vomit) to the act or taste of smoking, thus helping to decondition and extinguish the habit.

B

Behaviour therapy
A means of modifying behaviour by examining the symptoms of a particular problem, then employing various conditioning techniques to modify or remove these symptoms, such as flooding, reciprocal inhibition, aversion therapy, systematic desensitisation, massed practice and so forth.

Biofeedback
The use of electronic apparatus to give specific signals to indicate changes in the body. Through using this 'feedback' of information patients can learn to affect the normally autonomic processes like heart rate and blood pressure. Can be used in hypnosis to teach tense patients how to relax.

Birth trauma
Trauma and anxiety caused by the rigours of the birth process. A possible cause of some free floating anxiety. Re-birthing (developed by Leonard Orr) is designed to reconnect and release the patient from the effects of this trauma. In hypnosis the patient would be regressed to this birth time, with similar effects.

C

Case history
Details of the patient's life circumstances in general and specific particulars of their presenting problem. Usually taken before treatment commences, it can provide important pointers to the cause and cure of the problem. Never underestimate the value of a detailed case history.

Catalepsy
A condition observed in some forms of mental illness and also a phenomenon obtainable by hypnosis, where a patient's limb or limbs becomes rigid and can be placed in any position, where it will remain.

Catharsis
This word literally means 'purging' and describes the process of releasing repressed or pent-up emotional energy. This is usually affected by 'reliving', re-experiencing, acting out or talking out the memories of causal events.

Censor
According to psychoanalysis this is a psychological 'mechanism' which acts as a kind of filter or barrier to prevent repressed material or impulses from coming into consciousness.

Charming
Pre-Mesmer hypnosis, also animal hypnosis (snake charming, etc.).

Chevreul's pendulum
A simple method of determining or increasing a patient's suggestibility. A small pendulum is held over paper on which a cross (two intersecting lines) is drawn. Then the patient begins to swing the pendulum along one of the lines while the hypnotist suggests that it will begin to gradually move from its path until it is swinging along the path of the other line.

Clinical hypnosis
The process of carrying out therapy using hypnosis.

Closure
The completion of a psychological process. Developed in Gestalt psychology.

Complex
A psychological matrix of related emotional material. Term originating with Jung.

Compulsion
Where a patient feels an irresistible urge to carry out an act, whether a thought or a pattern of behaviour, even against his will (re: compulsive behaviour).

Concentration
The fixing of attention in one place or on one thing.

Conditioned reflex
Where an action is carried out in response to a trigger because the action and the trigger (stimuli) have become associated (conditioned). Term originating with Ivan P Pavlov.

Classical conditioning
The process of associating a stimulus with a response.

Contrasuggestibility
A rare but curious tendency in some patients to respond to a suggestion by acting out the opposite of its intention.

Counter suggestion
A suggestion given to neutralise a previous suggestion or belief.

Critical faculty
The ability to make a decision regarding the validity of a particular thing depends upon the exercise of the critical faculty. It is associated with the conscious mind and left hemisphere of the brain. Absence, of the critical faculty means that all 'proposals' are accepted as valid and as such is the temporary goal of hypnosis. Dreams are a good example of the state of the mind with the critical faculty in abeyance, as the most improbable things can take place in them but they seem perfectly realistic at the time.

D

Deepening
Once the trance state has been induced it can then be deepened. This usually takes the form of a simple count-down from ten to one (along with suitably relaxing suggestions), or perhaps some form of guided imagery, such as descending a long flight of stairs.

Defence mechanism
Usually associated with the 'censor' it is a psychological strategy to prevent painful, repressed or unpleasant material from coming to consciousness, where it might have to be faced and dealt with.

Dehypnotisation
Bringing the hypnotic state to an end and waking the patient. Usually arranged to happen at a particular signal, such as the count from one to five. Always remember to remove or nullify suggestions that you do not intend to remain.

Dental hypnosis
Typically hypnosis used to minimise the pain of dental surgery or to overcome a patient's morbid fear of dentistry.

Depersonalisation
A psychological condition common to many mental illnesses but one which can also be brought about in deep hypnosis when amnesia robs the patient of his immediate personal identity.

Desensitisation
Desensitisation (systematic) is a therapeutic method developed in behaviour therapy (by Joseph Wolpe) whereby the patient is gradually exposed to the source of his anxiety while engaging in anxiety-inhibiting behaviour, such as deep muscle relaxation. Thereby affecting deconditioning. Hypnosis can be combined to good effect with systematic desensitisation to form the therapy of hypno-desensitisation.

Diagnosis
The process of discerning the nature of an ailment.

Direct suggestion
An openly stated hypnotic command, direct, authoritative and without guile. Its meaning can be taken at face value. In contrast to indirect suggestion.

Dominant effect (the Law of)
Simply states that a strong emotion will always displace a weaker one (the rule being that only one emotional state can exist in experience at any one time). Try to evoke and connect emotion to your suggestions and they will be much more effective. Also, to move a feeling or emotion out of experience, evoke a stronger one. It is difficult to feel anxious when you are angry or happy.

E

Echolalia
Also known as 'echophrasia'. Where the hypnotised subject automatically repeats the words of the hypnotist (even when the words make no sense or are in a foreign language) in parrot fashion.

Ego
Freud proposed the Ego as part of the mind in direct interface with reality balancing the urges of the Id and the demands of the Super-Ego. More commonly accepted to mean the patient's sense of self.

Egocentricity
Acting as if the world revolves around the self and the self is the centre of the world.

Eidetic
Refers to eidetic memory and eidetic imagery. Commonly known as 'photographic memory'. Can be induced in deep hypnosis, to the point where (with fantasy) it becomes hallucination.

Engram
The name given to the idea that memory is stored 'traces' or 'images' in the brain. Thus memories are stored in engrams.

Eye fixation
Simply having the subject fix their gaze on a point (to narrow and focus their attention).

Eye closure
The point in hypnotic induction when subjects can no longer keep their eyes open. At this point the hypnotist has achieved eye closure.

Eyelid catalepsy
A good test of receptivity to suggestion and eyelid relaxation. The subject is told after eye closure that their eyelids are so relaxed that they cannot open them (sometimes the subject is also asked to look upwards as if at a point on their forehead). When this is shown to be the case, eyelid catalepsy has been achieved.

Epinosic
The psychoanalytical term for secondary gain.

Erethism
Where a part of the body becomes extremely sensitive, can have organic causes or can be induced by in hypnosis.

Erotophobia
Irrational fear of sexual stimuli or arousal.

Expectation

Expectation is an important factor to take into account before beginning hypnosis. If the patient expects to be successfully hypnotised he probably will be. Also in pre-induction talks always take the time to ensure patients have realistic idea of what the hypnotic state will be like and what the likely outcome of it will be.

Extinction

The term given to the process of deconditioning a reflex, more commonly known as 'breaking a habit'. The condition is said to be made extinct.

Extravert

A term originally coined by Jung which has passed into popular parlance to describe an outward-going personality type. As opposed to Introvert.

F

Fascination

The process of bringing about a hypnotic state by fixing the gaze on a point (typically a small shiny object). Also animal hypnosis.

Fight or flight

The fight or flight response represents the two basic choices (supervised by the autonomic nervous system) that we have in response to an alarming development. These instinctive choices were once necessary for our survival in an early predatory environment but are largely obsolete in the modern civilised world. They remain as options that can rarely be taken and severe stress can result from these natural impulses being thwarted.

Filter theory

The theory that the hypnotic state is a result of the mind's attention becoming more and more selective and narrow in its focus. Whether this is fixation on an external object, the sound of the practitioner's voice or fixation on the process of relaxation, the subject can eventually filter out almost everything, including the critical faculty. The mind becomes absorbed in the 'tension' of attention.

Fixation

In hypnosis, focusing of the attention at a singular point. In psychoanalysis, the arresting of development at a particular point.

Free association

Technique originating in psychoanalysis, which is now commonly used in many therapies where the intention is to arrive at memories and ideas that are not available to conscious recollection. Stimulus words are given to which the patient responds with the first word that is evoked. Sometimes used in hypno-analysis.

Fractionation

In hypnosis, this is a method of induction (Vogt's fractionation method) where the subject is partially relaxed then roused and asked to recount the sensations experienced. Then the hypnosis/relaxation continues again, often with the practitioner 'feeding back' the recounted experience and leading the patient still deeper. The patient is then roused again and his experiences sought, before the hypnosis resumes once again. The process continues until a deep trance state is obtained.

Functional disorders
These are problems which affect the physical body but have a psychological origin.

Fusion
In hypnotic practice this is the process of joining two or more normally disparate concepts, feelings or even memories of experience to form a new experience. For a simple example – if a patient feels anxiety at the sight of a cat but can clearly remember the feeling of happiness at receiving a special gift then ideo-fusion can be used in hypnosis to connect the image of a cat to the feeling of pleasure at receiving a gift, by having the patient summon both image and sensation at the same time.

G

Group hypnosis
Refers to the effect perceived that hypnosis of people in large groups often results in greater depth of success, perhaps because the members of the group 'feedback' from each other. Mass hypnosis is a recognised phenomenon. Not normally used in therapy, which needs to be tailored to specific patients; it is used at religious and political gatherings to get simple ideas accepted at the group level.

Galvanometer
A device which measures the galvanic skin response. This response is a small change of electrical conductivity of the skin, due in part to the presence of stress. Used as the basis of lie detection equipment it is used by some hypno-analysts to detect areas of conflict and stress as patients recount their personal history.

Generalisation
A psychological process often uncovered by hypnosis, at the root of many phobias and neuroses. It is part of the normal learning function but can lead to error due to unchecked extrapolation. As a simple example – you are tormented as a child by a bully with red hair, which leads to the unconscious generalisation that all persons with red hair are tormentors. Thus you might feel anxiety in the presence of a red-haired person, even if you have not met them before. It can develop even further as the colour red itself develops into a stimulus for anxiety even though it is no longer connected to a person but to some other object.

Glossolalia
Where a person 'babbles' or speaks in some unknown tongue, usually while believing perfect sense is being made. Can be a symptom of religious hysteria and mental disorder but can also be made to occur by suggestion in deep hypnosis.

Gnosis
From the Greek word for knowledge. In clinical hypnosis it refers to the uncovering of a piece of information or personal experience which enables a dynamic re-evaluation, leading to rapid improvement, or cessation of presenting problems. Axial information.

H

Hallucination
A hallucination can be described as an experience of one or more senses which occurs without an external stimulation. In other words the cause of the sensory activation is internal and is common in psychosis and drug misuse. The phenomenon can be evoked in the deeper states of hypnosis and also with direct electrical stimulation of the brain. Positive hallucination describes the process of experiencing something that is not actually present. Negative hallucination describes the process of not experiencing something that is present.

Hand clasp test
This test of susceptibility is common in stage hypnosis but little used in therapy. Quite simply the subject is asked to clasp his hands together by interlocking the fingers. The hypnotist might then make suggestions that the hands are sticking together, tighter and tighter. Eventually the subject is told flatly that his hands are locked together and he will not be able to separate them until the hypnotist gives that instruction. If the subject is unable to part his hands, or has some difficulty in this act, he is judged to be susceptible to hypnotic suggestion at that time.

Hetero-hypnosis
This is simply the process of a hypnotist hypnotising a subject or subjects, as opposed to self-hypnosis.

Hidden observer
An occasional phenomenon experienced in hypnosis in which a part of the mind seems to watch the proceedings in a detached and passive way, even though the rest of the body and personality might be engaged in carrying out some hypnotic suggestion.

Hyperaesthesia
Vivification of the senses. Can be achieved with hypnosis.

Hyperamnesia
Where amnesia is the partial or total inability to recall memories, hyperamnesia is the opposite, an increase of the ability to remember.

Hypersuggestibility
A phenomenon of deep hypnosis characterised by the increase of suggestibility.

Hypnogogic
Brief hypnotic state passed through on the way to natural sleep.

Hypnoanalysis
The process of examining the personal history of a patient using regression, which is facilitated by hypnosis.

Hypnogenic
Describes something which produces the hypnotic state.

Hypnotic
A state characteristic of the light hypnotic state.

Hypnoplasty
Similar to automatic writing under hypnosis but clay or plasticene is used by the patient to make images or objects.

Hypnopompic
Brief hypnotic state passed through on the way from natural sleep to wakefulness.

Hypnosis
The process of obtaining a special condition of cooperation, acceptance and partial critical abeyance brought about through a combination of induction, motivation, expectation and trust. Results in a hypnotic state.

Hypnotic
As relating to the process of obtaining a hypnotic state.

Hypnotic trance
See 'Trance'.

I

Ideomotor response
Literally a physical response to an idea. Used in hypnosis for signalling. Typically the index fingers of each hand are designated 'yes' and 'no' values and the control of these fingers is passed to the hypnotised patient's subconscious mind, which then responds to questions by moving the 'Yes' or 'No' finger.

Implosion therapy
Also known as 'flooding', a practice originating with behaviour therapy. The patient is exposed to the source of anxiety (for example) without aversive consequences, until the fear eventually subsides.

Impotence
Sexual impotence is the inability of the male to have an erection. Where this

problem has a psychological origin it can be treated successfully with hypnosis.

Induction
Hypnotic induction describes the process used in the transition of the subject from normal waking consciousness into the 'hypnotic state'.

Introvert
A term originally coined by Jung which has passed into popular parlance to describe an inwardly focused personality type. As opposed to Extrovert.

J

James, William
An American (1842–1910), one of the fathers of psychology. Author of *The Principles of Psychology*, which helped to establish psychology as a science and influence many of the seminal thinkers of that period.

Jehovah complex
Megalomania. Identification with God or supreme being.

Jung, Carl Gustav
Swiss psychiatrist (1875–1961), collaborated with Sigmund Freud (1907–1912) to expand the theory of psychoanalysis. In 1912 he broke from Freud to develop his own significant branch of psychoanalysis called analytical psychology.

K

Kent–Rosanoff list
This is a list of words for use in free association which the authors have thoroughly tested and analysed, especially the frequency of various responses. Thus the results of a free association session with the words on the list can be compared against previous results (taken from people in different known psychological states). Not normally used in clinical hypnosis but may have some application in hypno-analysis.

Kinaesthetic memory
Physical memory, of bodily states, positions, movements and sensations. Used frequently in hypnosis, especially during induction when bodily states are evoked by suggestion.

L

Lachrymal glands
The small glands that are responsible for tear production. They often become active as hypnosis deepens.

Latent time
The time between stimulus and response. A period often extended as hypnosis deepens.

Lethargy
Early term coined by JM Charcot for the light or early stage of hypnosis.

Levitation
Where a limb is caused to rise by suggestion. Often used in hypnotic induction and deepening. Useful where the ensuing therapy employs partial dissociation or glove anaesthesia.

Liminal
The threshold.

Liminal sensitivity
The threshold of sensation. The minimum stimulus required to cause sensation. Hence 'subliminal' – beneath the threshold of sensation.

Locus of control
The place where a person experiences the controlling influence in their life to emanate from. A person with an internal locus of control feels that they control their life from within themselves and are responsible for all things that happen to them. A person with an external locus of control feels that their life is governed by forces external to them over which they have no real influence.

M

Magnetism
See 'Animal magnetism'.

Mass hypnosis
Where a large group of people simultaneously experience a state of heightened suggestibility and become open to the experience of hypnotic phenomenon.

Massed practice
A technique borrowed from behaviour therapy, where a patient is encouraged, either in or out of hypnosis, to purposefully repeat his symptom(s) over and over. A typical use might be for a facial tick. The unconscious stimulus becomes exhausted (extinct) by the conscious repetition.

Memory manipulation
Under hypnosis memories can be enhanced, removed or even changed. This facility of hypnosis is often used in therapy.

Mesmerism
The type of 'hypnosis' that was practised by Mesmer and his followers. Typically

theatrical and involving the use of 'hypnotic passes', where the hands are moved along the shape of the body as if combing some invisible medium. Still practised today in eastern countries and in parts of Russia. Making something of a revival in some parts of America, mainly due to immigrants bringing these skills with them and the growing 'new age' belief in spiritual healing.

Monoideism
Describes a state of fixation on a single thought or topic. Encountered in hypnosis as concentration increases. Term coined by James Braid.

Mythomania
Imaginary rationalisation of acts and exaggerations on suggested themes, often encountered in deep hypnosis.

N

Nancy School
Early French school of psychotherapy founded in 1866 by AA Liebault (in the city of Nancy). Hypnosis played a great part in the treatment methodology and much research was conducted into this subject, particularly by HM Bernheim.

Negative hallucination
Not seeing something that is actually there. Often used in stage hypnosis.

Negativism
A form of resistance to suggestions. Can be so strong that the opposite course of action to the one suggested is taken (active negativism). Simply refusing to accept suggestions is termed 'passive negativism'.

Nervous sleep
The term coined by J Braid to describe hypnosis.

Neurosis
A functional problem of entirely psychogenic origin, often manifesting as mal-adaptive habit(s). Usually treatable by clinical hypnosis.

Nightmare
A dream that arouses great fear and alarm.

O

Obsession
A persistently recurring idea, compelling and difficult to put out of mind.

Obsessive compulsive
In obsessive compulsive neurosis the patient feels compelled to carry out the

persistently recurring idea. This can take many forms, such as excessive hand washing (sometimes the patient feeling the need to wash hands more than 100 times per day) or excessive checking of door locks or clothing, etc. Treatable with hypnosis.

Oneirosis
An early term for a stage of light hypnosis, similar to hypnogogic state and characterised by visual imagery. From the Greek word *oneiros*, meaning dreams.

Operator
A name occasionally given to the hypnotist.

Oedipus complex
A term coined by Sigmund Freud (from a Greek myth) to describe the complex formed in young males through a form of sexual attraction to the mother, causing jealousy of the father and resulting in a feeling of conflict and guilt. In the Greek myth Oedipus killed his father and unknowingly married his mother.

One trial learning
A single occurrence or event that has such a powerful impact on the patient that it modifies their behaviour from then onwards. For example, a person becoming violently ill through drinking too much whisky might be unable thereafter to drink whisky again.

Operant conditioning
A form of learning identified in Behaviourism (BF Skinner) in which a person's behaviour (or any animal's for that matter) is modified by positive or negative reinforcement (such as praise or punishment).

Overcompensation
Conscious or unconscious behaviour designed to make amends for (or disguise) some (real or imagined) shortcoming.

P

Painless surgery
It is quite possible to undergo surgery using hypnosis as the only anaesthetic.

Paradoxical sleep
Another name for rapid eye movement (REM) sleep.

Paramnesia
Distorted memories rather than lost memories (as with amnesia).

Pavlov, Ivan P
Russian physiologist (1849–1936). Won a Nobel Prize in 1904 for his work on the digestion system. Became well-known for his experiments into conditioning.

Peripheral nervous system
That part of the total nervous system which connects the sensory systems of the body to the central nervous system (brain and spinal cord).

Phobia
An intense fear or morbid dread. Treatable with hypnosis.

Perls, Fritz
Born in Germany. Originally a psychoanalyst, he went on to develop Gestalt therapy.

Photoma
Optical hallucination, sparks or points of light. Sometimes reported in hypnosis.

Placebo
A placebo is usually a medical prescription given with the idea of producing beneficial results by utilising the patient's belief that he has been given useful medicine. The placebo does not have any medical potency of a chemical nature and relies for its effect on suggestion. It is sometimes given as part of an experiment to determine the effectiveness of a new drug, the group given the placebo being the control. It is recognised by medical authorities that as much as 30% of the effectiveness of any particular drug is due to the placebo effect.

Post-hypnotic
Literally, after hypnosis. Post-hypnotic suggestions for example, are suggestions given by the hypnotist to the subject to be carried out later, after the hypnotic session has been terminated.

Postural sway test
A simple test of hypnotic susceptibility. The subject is asked to stand erect with feet together and eyes closed. He is then asked to recall a time as a child when he swung back and forth on a swing. If the subject has good powers of imagination and concentration he will begin to swing perceptibly back and forth.

Prestige
Prestige is valuable to a hypnotist and is the esteem with which a patient holds his abilities. The hypnotist should always seek to maintain a smart, professional image in order to encourage and maintain a sense of prestige.

Psychoanalysis
Developed by Sigmund Freud and his followers. Based on the idea that neurotic and maladaptive behaviour is caused by emotional and instinctive energies that become repressed in the patients unconscious. Therapy takes place when these repressed elements are brought to consciousness and catharsis takes place. Usually involves an extensive case history being taken, along with dream analysis.

Psychodrama
A technique of working with a group devised originally by JL Moreno, in which members of the gathering 'act out' their problems as if in real life.

Psychogenic
Of psychological origin.

Psychosomatic
Effects in the body originating in the mind.

Q

Quantum psychology
A fusion of Eastern philosophy, Western psychology and quantum physics.

Questioning
The method of giving suggestions via the medium of structured questions. This takes advantage of latent affirmative response, that is, 'Would you like to be more confident?' elicits a conscious and/or unconscious yes, which affirms the content of the suggestion at an unconscious level. The straightforward, 'You are going to feel more confident' may be denied by the immediate experience of the patient even though the critical faculty is diminished.

R

Rapport
Describes the feeling of trust, cooperation and acceptance that can exist between hypnotist and subject. Once rapport is established susceptibility to suggestion increases greatly.

Rationalisation
From a psychological point of view rationalisation is the process of explaining an action in terms of its reasonableness. Usually this is an action that the patient is not particularly proud of but hopes to diminish feelings of guilt by showing the act to follow natural logic. Specious excuse. From a hypnosis point of view rationalisation is where a subject seeks to explain his actions in hypnosis or post-hypnotic suggestion in a 'reasonable fashion'. For example, a subject is hypnotised and told that every time the hypnotist claps his hands the subject will remove his jacket. This suggestion can be tested several times and each time the subject will remove his jacket but when asked why he keeps doing this he will rationalise and say something like, 'It keeps getting warm in here,' or 'I don't feel comfortable wearing it.'

Reciprocal inhibition
A term from behaviour therapy which is defined because of its use within hypno-desensitisation. Reciprocal inhibition occurs when an anxiety-inducing stimulus is made to happen at the same time as an anxiety-inhibiting response (such as deep relaxation), then the anxiety-inducing stimulus will begin to lose its ability to evoke anxiety. For example, if a patient is made to relax completely while experiencing something that would normally make them anxious

or provoke a phobic reaction, the ability of that thing to cause a reaction will be diminished.

Rehearsal
The method of obtaining psychological experience by practising events in imagination as if they were actually occurring. Useful for goal orientation.

Relaxation
Removing the will to move (or state of readiness) from the body's muscles. Lack of tension, leading to a comfortable stillness.

REM sleep
Rapid eye movement sleep, characteristic of the dream state.

Repression
One of the earliest concepts of psychoanalysis. The theory is that a psychic function exists which seeks to prevent certain emotionally charged memories from coming to consciousness by keeping them deep in the unconscious mind. It is claimed that these 'repressed memories' are the dynamic source of neurosis and maladapted behaviour. Whether there is such a repressing function is open to debate; nevertheless the mind does seem to work as if there is. Experience has proven that unearthing and expressing the energy of these 'imprisoned' memories can lead to the relief of symptoms.

Resistance
In hypnosis this refers to the opposition sometimes faced by hypnotists when trying to induce hypnosis in a subject. This is usually unconscious resistance due to deep-rooted fear or distrust and so can occur even when the subject consciously desires to be hypnotised. The hypnotist will need to establish strong rapport and work on the fear first. Every normally functioning human can be hypnotised.

Reticular activating system (RAS)
Refers to a part of the brain which functions to govern wakefulness and sleep.

Retrograde amnesia
Inability to recall memories before a certain event. For example, a person might not be able to remember anything that happened before an accident but can remember everything that has happened since.

Reverie
When the mind drifts into daydreams or fantasy.

Revivification
Literally, to bring back to life or reanimate. Refers to regression experience where the subject fully re-experiences that time and adopts all the characteristics of the period. For example a subject regressed to the age of five who is revivifying has no memory of anything after that age and will speak, act and think as a five-year-old.

S

Salpetriere School
Salpetriere School of hypnosis. A school of psychopathology operated by JM Charcot, whose views on hypnosis influenced Sigmund Freud. Charcot believed that hypnosis was due to a form of hysteria.

Schizophrenia
A serious mental disorder which affects the sufferer's ability to deal with reality. Usually ascribed to dissociation, splitting of consciousness.

Script
In hypnosis this term is usually used to describe a pre-prepared induction or deepener.

Secondary gain
Every cloud has a silver lining! Nobody really wants a problem but sometimes a problem can have a small advantage attached to it and it is this advantage that is described by the term 'secondary gain'. For example, no-one wants a painful headache but it may have the secondary gain benefit of getting some attention.

Selective amnesia
Inability to recall memories about a specific thing. Often used as a demonstration of hypnotic phenomena where a subject might be told to forget a number between one and five, and then asked to count the fingers on his hand!

Selective attention
The natural ability of people to select which incoming information they will consciously receive. We perceive much more than we realise but something within us decides what is important to notice. Normally an unconscious process it can be temporarily explored consciously. The manipulation of selective attention is thought to be important to achieving a hypnotic state.

Self-hypnosis
Where a person enters a hypnotic state under their own guidance, without using an external hypnotist. Also called 'auto-hypnosis'.

Signalling
Usually called ideo-motor response signalling (IMR). Where a small bodily movement is used for communication.

State-dependent memory
Refers to memories which are dependent upon the replication of certain physiological 'contexts' before they can be recalled. For example, an event that takes place while the subject is heavily intoxicated or in a state of high emotion might be forgotten upon return to normality and can be recalled only when the non-ordinary state is re-experienced. To a certain extent all memory can be said to be state-dependent but fortunately for most people 'normal consciousness' is a steady state.

Subconscious
Mental processes that are not normally conscious, separate from consciousness. The word is often interchanged loosely with unconscious.

Subliminal
This literally means below the threshold of sensory awareness.

Suggestibility
Defines the extent to which a person will accept a proposal to be factual.

Suggestion
A proposal made to a person as fact, usually just before or during the hypnotic state. The purpose of which is usually to obtain a deeper hypnotic state, increase suggestibility or obtain some therapeutic change.

T

Tactile induction
The method of inducing hypnosis by gently stroking the subject's body, usually the forehead but can be almost any part of the body. Not often used in therapy these days, it has its roots in Mesmerism and animal hypnosis (trout tickling!).

Trance induction
The process of bringing about a 'hypnotic' state, either in oneself (self-hypnosis) or in another (hetero-hypnosis).

Transference
A word that has come to us from psychoanalysis and refers to the way that patients sometimes 'project' unconscious associations onto the practitioner. For example, patients may come to project emotional attachments that they cannot feel for a parent onto the practitioner. Usually only a problem when therapy is protracted.

Trauma
Shock to the person, either physical or psychological or both. Can have effects which endure beyond the immediate healing process.

U

Unconditioned response
An original or normal reflex to a stimulus, as opposed to a 'conditioned response', which is learned behaviour. A dog will normally salivate when it sees food and so this is an unconditioned response but with training the dog can be made to salivate in response to a bell ringing, this is a conditioned response.

Unconscious mind

The unconscious mind is a collective term which covers all the mental processes that are operating outside of immediate consciousness awareness. This has been likened to the iceberg metaphor where consciousness is represented by the one-seventh of the berg which stands above the waterline. The seven-eighths of the berg below the waterline representing the unconscious mind. Another analogy is the eating process, where eating represents the conscious processes while digestion, assimilation, is unconscious. There are areas where conscious and unconscious processes overlap. Breathing is such an example: most of the time we are unaware (unconscious) of our breathing, especially during sleep, but it is possible to consciously intercede and modify our breathing patterns. So it can be seen that we have unconscious processes that are so 'deep' that we are never consciously aware of them, whereas other unconscious processes are only unconscious because they are not 'in' consciousness, or temporarily forgotten.

A good example of an unconscious process, as something that continues even though we are no longer consciously aware of it, is afforded by the memory. You will no doubt have had the experience of trying to remember a particular name or fact but found that you were unable to do so. So you continue about your normal affairs and might think, or be consciously aware, of many other things when the name or fact suddenly 'pops' into your mind (consciousness) 'proving' that a process has taken place (unconscious search) beyond your conscious awareness (unconscious).

It is not clear which faculty decides whether a process will be unconscious or consciously available to us but it does seem that a 'need to know' rule applies.

Processes that we no longer need to know about (they are not a danger to us, or we have become so conditioned to them that the process can be carried out unconsciously) do gradually pass into the unconscious. Yet it seems that some non-conscious faculty or element is always vigilant. This is evident at a large gathering where you are struggling to make yourself heard and all you might consciously hear is a babble of background noise from the crowd, but if someone mentions your name you will suddenly become very conscious of it. Likewise a mother (until she has become conditioned otherwise) will awaken from deep sleep if her baby murmurs or moves.

Perhaps the most important fact from a psychological or hypno-therapeutic point of view is that the unconscious mind is the repository of memory. Thus therapy is usually a matter of investigating or modifying or bringing into consciousness some causal dynamic (usually trauma or false learning) which has become buried in the unconscious mind.

Psychoanalytic theory posits that there is some form of psychic filter which keeps 'un-faceable' memories connected with unpleasant events away from consciousness (repressed), hence the difficulty involved in recovering them. It may be that there is no such 'filter' but repression is simply a continuation of the mind's natural process of 'deconditioning' memories that are not often used.

If you require a particular fact (memory) every day it will become conditioned to appearing in consciousness and will be readily available for recall. In other words it is valued as important. A traumatic event is unpleasant and unless repeatedly bringing it to consciousness brings benefits it will naturally be 'forgotten' or deconditioned from consciousness.

Then there is the 'state-dependent' theory that works on the theory that memories do not exist in isolation but are a composite of external and internal states. With this theory, memories are recoverable while the patient is in, or near to, the external or internal state that they were in during the original learning experience. As an extreme example a person who was heavily intoxicated the previous night might have no memory of events that took place then, but if the patient returns to the intoxicated state then the memories can become available. Similarly, dreams are easily forgotten upon awakening (because the state has changed from sleep to wakefulness) and a way to retrieve them is to return the body to the exact position it was in on awakening. From this theory it can be seen that memories might not actually be screened by a filter but may be unavailable because of the difference between the physical and mental state at the present moment and the time at which the event occurred. Is there a simpler answer? The unconscious could be said to be everything that we are, but are not aware of.

V

Visualisation
Literally, the process of creating images with the imagination. Very useful for goal achievement and artificial experience through rehearsal.

Visual predilection
It became recognised in the psychological research of the 1950s that unconscious eye movements often gave evidence of categories of mental processes or neurological activities. Studies of these findings by Richard Bandler and John Grinder eventually developed to become part of the technical knowledge of neuro-linguistic programming (NLP). It was recognised that people generally fall into three groups of cognitive emphasis: visual–auditory–kinaesthetic. That is, some people's mental experience is largely visual, others' auditory and others' kinaesthetic. These different types may be recognised by observing eye cues in response to questions.

W

Waking hypnosis
A state of rapport which allows suggestions to be effectively given to the subject, without the need for formal trance induction.

Y

Yes set
Refers to a technique outlined by M Erickson where the conversation between the practitioner and patient is intentionally structured in such a way that the

patient must respond with the word 'yes' (in other words, obtaining a positive rather than a negative response). This sets a positive mood for interaction and begins the reframing process.

It is also possible to use the momentum of the repetitive response to have someone agree to something without full consideration. Sales people often utilise this technique by asking a series of innocuous questions for which the answer can only be 'yes' followed quickly by a line such as 'So you want to buy this then?' when the unwary will often answer 'yes' without due thought.

Appendix III: Useful contacts and website addresses

Thames Medical Lectures (www.thamesmedicallectures.com)

Hypnosis training for healthcare professionals

A not-for-profit organisation set up by the author to promote excellence in medical education. It provides training courses for medical in clinical hypnosis, language and communication, stress management and goal setting, as well as specialist modules in medical schools. It provides special study modules at UK medical schools.

Postgraduate workshops for medical professionals are available in:

- clinical hypnosis basic theory and practice
- clinical hypnosis and pain control
- clinical hypnosis in general practice
- clinical hypnosis and habit-breaking
- clinical hypnosis in psychiatry
- clinical hypnosis and obsessive compulsive disorders
- clinical hypnosis in oncology
- clinical hypnosis in anxiety disorders.

Hypnodontics (www.hypnodontics.co.uk)

Clinical hypnosis in dentistry

A specialist training organisation for dentists, with workshops in all aspects of clinical hypnosis in dentistry, including needle phobias, dental anxiety, hypno-anaesthesia and teaching self-hypnosis.

Hypnova (www.hypnova.com)

Training courses in hypnosis for pregnancy and childbirth

Training provider specialising in clinical hypnosis workshops for women. University accredited training courses for midwives and hypnotherapists in the use of clinical hypnosis techniques for childbirth are also available.

Workshops include:

- fertility and conception
- pregnancy and childbirth
- menopause
- professional training for midwives and hypnotherapists in the use of clinical hypnosis for childbirth.

Hypnosis CDs suitable for children

www.firstwayforward.com/childcds.html

Clear Goal Concept (www.cleargoalconcept.com)

Hypnosis workshops and CDs

Clinical hypnosis compact discs on subjects from smoking cessation, weight loss, motivation, pain control, better sleep, health and wellbeing, and more. Contact details for consultations with the author or her team are also on the website.
  Workshops include:

- self-hypnosis
- personal goal setting
- personal stress management
- reading people – a guide to body language
- trichotillomania
- phobias.

Stop Smoking Clinic (www.stopsmokingatonce.co.uk)

Smoking cessation

The author's smoking cessation clinic in central London.

London College of Clinical Hypnosis (www.lcch.co.uk)

Professional clinical hypnosis training

A widely respected teaching organisation, presenting professional training courses throughout the UK and in Portugal.

European Journal of Clinical Hypnosis (www.ejch.com)

Peer-reviewed journal of clinical hypnosis

A journal (hard copy) covering many of the wider aspects of using hypnosis as a psychological intervention. Many contributions by noted medical professionals – some articles online.

British Society of Clinical Hypnosis (www.bsch.org.uk)

Clinical hypnosis association

An organisation dedicated to establishing high standards of ethical practice within hypnotherapy. The website contains a continually updated and fully searchable database of skilled hypnotherapists.

Dr Michael Yapko (www.yapko.com)

Depression specialist

Dr Yapko is one of the modern innovators in clinical hypnotherapy. He writes and teaches widely, and is a recognised specialist in the use of hypnosis to treat depression.

Milton Erickson Foundation (www.erickson-foundation.org)

Ericksonian hypnosis establishment

Dr Milton Erickson has become something of a legendary figure in modern hypnotherapy. He pioneered the use of 'indirect' hypnotic techniques during the later half of the 20th century and introduced many paradoxical techniques which have been expanded upon since that time.

Online hypnosis journal (www.hypnogenesis.com)

Hypnosis magazine

A body of articles about hypnosis and hypnotherapy contributed by hypnotherapists from around the world. The basis idea being to demystify the subject and broaden its interest to the general public.

Royal College of Psychiatrists (www.rcpsych.ac.uk)

Psychiatrists

The website of the Royal College of Psychiatrists. Information about many disorders.

British Association of Medical Hypnosis (BAMH) www.bamh.org

Association of doctors, dentists and hypnotherapy professionals. Register of practising members and professional journal (*European Journal of Clinical Hypnosis*).

The British Society of Medical and Dental Hypnosis (BSMDH) www.bsmdh.org

BSMDH is a national organisation of doctors, dentists and other health professionals within the NHS who are trained and interested in hypnosis.

British Society of Experimental and Clinical Hypnosis (BSECH) www bsech.com

Doctors, dentists and psychologists interested in the theory, research and practice of hypnosis and related procedures.

International Society of Hypnosis (ISH) www.ish.unimelb.edu.au/ish.html

Dedicated to improving clinical practice and research, as well as both formal and informal communication pertinent to the scientific use of hypnosis.

The Royal Society of Medicine (RSM) www.rsm.ac.uk/academ/sech_p.htm

The RSM has a Hypnosis and Psychosomatic Medicine section for medical practitioners interested in the subject.

Index